GARDENERS' WORLD
DIRECTORY

Compiled by

Geoff Hamilton

BBC BOOKS

Published by BBC Books,
a division of BBC Enterprises Limited,
Woodlands, 80 Wood Lane
London W12 0TT

First Published 1993

© Geoff Hamilton 1993

ISBN 0 563 36230 8

Maps by Rodney Paull
Drawings by Peter Bailey

Printed and bound in Great Britain by
Butler & Tanner Ltd, Frome

Cover printed by Clays Ltd, St Ives Plc

Contents

Introduction

The *Gardeners' World* office receives hundreds of letters every single week of the year. Most of them are seeking advice and information. Where can I buy the product you showed last week? How far apart should I sow my carrots? Will little Johnnie be ill if he eats laburnum seeds? Where can I get further information about allotments? Gardeners are hungry for information and we are delighted to try to help.

Alas, because we get so many requests, we sometimes take quite a long time to provide the information. We apologize for that and hope that this little book will go some way to rectifying the problem.

In it you will find all those handy facts and figures you so often need to get your gardening just right and to make it that much more successful. But we also hope it will give you some inspiration.

If you want to know what to plant in that shady corner, you will find dozens of suitable plants listed. If you get hooked on a particular species of plant and want to find out more, well the addresses of the relevant society or perhaps the National Plant Collection will enable you to do so. And, if you want to know where to buy unusual plants, we can help there too.

This is also a very personal book. At Barnsdale I test dozens of new products each year and I have my own favourite old ones too. While I in no way want to suggest that the tools, equipment and sundries I use are the *only* satisfactory ones, at least you can be sure that those listed have done the job for me over the years. And as you can imagine, most of the gear used at Barnsdale gets a pretty rugged trial. I have marked the relevant products with a Barnsdale Recommended rosette.

Mind you, I know jolly well that there are some first rate gardeners amongst our viewers so I wouldn't dream of inflicting my own preferences on you to the exclusion of all else. So, if you want to control whitefly you'll find my favourite organic control, but you'll also be able to look up the appropriate chemical.

Finally, may I ask a favour? We intend to update our directory regularly so there is constant room for improvement. If there are facts missing that you'd like included, I'd be grateful if you would spare a minute to drop me a line to let me know.

I hope you'll find the *Gardeners' World Directory* useful.

Geoff Hamilton

Television and Radio Programmes

Television and radio companies, including the BBC, tend to make up their minds about programmes at the last minute. We have listed all the information available about BBC programmes at the time of going to press but you must check the *Radio Times* for further details and for details of other programmes.

Most programmes welcome letters from their viewers, whether it be queries, complaints, or even praise! If you want to get in touch, write to the producer or the presenter of the programme. But do bear in mind that, if other programmes receive the same amount of mail as there is in the *Gardeners' World* postbag, you may wait some time before receiving a reply.

BBC Addresses

London
Television Centre, Wood Lane, London W12 7RJ

Birmingham
BBC Broadcasting Centre, Pebble Mill Road, Birmingham B5 7SA

Edinburgh
Broadcasting House, Queen St, Edinburgh EH2 1JF

Norwich
St Catherine's Close, All Saints Green, Norwich, Norfolk NR1 3ND

Plymouth
Broadcasting House, Seymour Road, Mannamead, Plymouth PL3 5BD

ITV Company Addresses

Anglia Television Ltd
Anglia House, Norwich NR1 3JG
and
48 Leicester Square, London WC2H 7FB

Border Television plc
The Television Centre, Carlisle CA1 3NT

Carlton Television Ltd
101 St Martin's Lane, London WC2N 4AZ

Central Independent Television plc
Central House, Broad St, Birmingham B1 2JP
and
East Midlands TV Centre, Lenton Lane, Nottingham NG7 2NA
and

35–38 Portman Square, London
W1A 2HZ

Channel Television
Television Centre, La Pouquelaye, St
Helier, Jersey JE2 3ZD Channel
Islands

GMTV
The London Television Centre, Upper
Ground, London SE1 9LT

Grampian Television plc
Queen's Cross, Aberdeen AB9 2XJ

Granada Television Ltd
Granada Television Centre, Quay St,
Manchester M60 9EA
and
36 Golden Square, London
W1R 4AH

HTV Ltd
HTV Wales, The Television Centre,
Culverhouse Cross, Cardiff CF5 6XJ
and
The Television Centre, Bath Road,
Bristol BS4 3HG
and
99 Baker St, London W1M 2AJ

London Weekend Television Ltd
South Bank Television Centre, Kent
House, Upper Ground, London
SE1 9LT

Meridian Broadcasting Ltd
Television Centre, Northam,
Southampton SO9 5HZ
and
36–38 Southampton St, London
WC2E 7HE

Scottish Television plc
Cowcaddens, Glasgow G2 3PR
and
114 St Martin's Lane, London
WC2N 4AZ

Tyne Tees Television Ltd
The Television Centre, City Road,
Newcastle upon Tyne NE1 2AL
and
15 Bloomsbury Square, London
WC1A 2LJ

Ulster Television plc
Havelock House, Ormeau Road,
Belfast, Northern Ireland BT1 1EB
and
West Gate, West World, London
W5 1EH

Westcountry Television Ltd
c/o Brittany Ferries, Millbay Docks,
Plymouth PL1 3EW
and
99 Charterhouse St, London
EC1M 6AB

Yorkshire Television Ltd
The Television Centre, Leeds
LS3 1JS
and
Television House, 32 Bedford Row,
London WC1R 4HE

Channel Four Television Company Ltd
60 Charlotte St, London W1P 2AX

Programmes

BBC 1

Good Morning
See *Radio Times* for details
Stephan Buczacki (fortnightly on Fridays)

EAST ANGLIA
Look East
See *Radio Times* for details
Peter Seabrook

SCOTLAND
The Beechgrove Garden
See *Radio Times* for details
Sid Robertson
Carole Baxter
Bill Torrance

BBC 2

Gardeners' World
Fri 8.30 p.m. *repeated* Mon
5.30 p.m.
Geoff Hamilton
Liz Rigbey and team

SCOTLAND
The Beechgrove Garden Live Phone-in
team as above
See *Radio Times* for details
Phone: 0224 625900

BBC National Radio

BBC Broadcasting House, Portland
Place, London W1A 1AA

RADIO 4
FM 92.4–94.6
LW 198 kHz (1515 m)
Gardeners' Question Time Sun 2.00
p.m. *repeated* Wed 11.30 a.m.
PO Box 27, Manchester M60 1SJ
Clay Jones
Stefan Buczacki
Sue Phillips
Fred Downham
Daphne Ledward
The Gardening Quiz
See *Radio Times* for details
Stephan Buczacki and guests

RADIO 5
MW 909, 693 kHz (330, 433 m)
Weekend Edition Sun 7.15 a.m.
(fortnightly)
Richard Jackson

Key to radio stations

Channel Islands
1 BBC Radio Jersey
2 BBC Radio Guernsey

South
3 BBC Radio Cornwall
4 BBC Radio Devon (Plymouth)
5 BBC Radio Devon
6 BBC Somerset Sound
7 BBC Radio Bristol
8 BBC Wiltshire Sound
9 BBC Radio Solent
10 BBC Radio Oxford
11 BBC Radio Bedfordshire
12 Greater London Radio
13 BBC Radio Kent
14 BBC Radio Sussex

Midlands and Eastern Counties
15 BBC Essex
16 BBC Radio Suffolk
17 BBC Radio Norfolk
18 BBC Radio Cambridgeshire
19 BBC Radio Peterborough
20 BBC Radio Lincolnshire
21 BBC Radio Northampton
22 BBC Radio Leicester
23 BBC Radio Nottingham
24 BBC CWR
25 BBC Radio Derby
26 BBC Radio Gloucestershire
27 BBC Radio Hereford and Worcester
28 BBC Radio WM
29 BBC Radio Stoke
30 BBC Radio Shropshire

Wales
31 BBC Radio Wales
32 BBC Radio Cymru
33 BBC Radio Clwyd

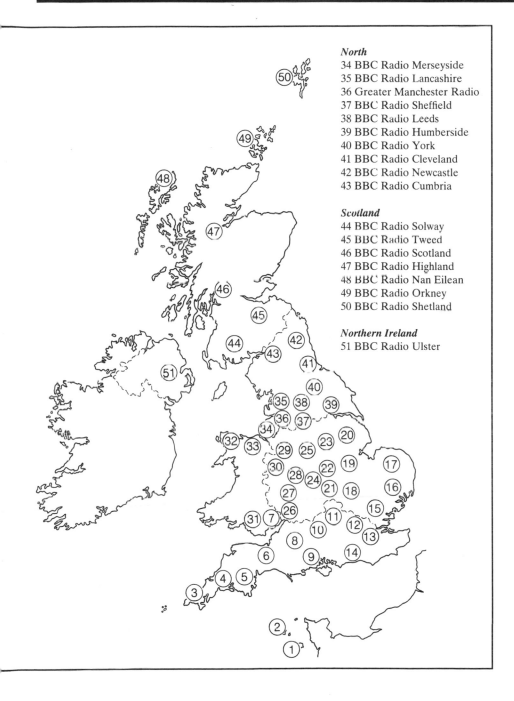

North
34 BBC Radio Merseyside
35 BBC Radio Lancashire
36 Greater Manchester Radio
37 BBC Radio Sheffield
38 BBC Radio Leeds
39 BBC Radio Humberside
40 BBC Radio York
41 BBC Radio Cleveland
42 BBC Radio Newcastle
43 BBC Radio Cumbria

Scotland
44 BBC Radio Solway
45 BBC Radio Tweed
46 BBC Radio Scotland
47 BBC Radio Highland
48 BBC Radio Nan Eilean
49 BBC Radio Orkney
50 BBC Radio Shetland

Northern Ireland
51 BBC Radio Ulster

BBC Local Radio

CHANNEL ISLANDS

BBC RADIO GUERNSEY
FM 93.2
MW 1116 kHz
Commerce House, Les Banques,
St Peter Port, Guernsey
Tel: (0481) 728977
Phone-in: (0481) 728888
Lunch Break Thurs 1.15 p.m.
Ian Curle

BBC RADIO JERSEY
FM 88.8
MW 1026 kHz
Broadcasting House, Rouge Bouillon,
St Helier, Jersey
Tel: (0534) 70000
Phone-in: (0534) 20255
Jersey Today Thurs 8.20 a.m. *repeated*
Thurs 5.15 p.m.
Denis Shaw
Lunch Break Fri 1.05 p.m. (monthly)
Denis Shaw

SOUTH WEST

BBC RADIO BRISTOL
FM 95.5 Bristol 94.9 Bath 104.6
MW Avon: 1548 kHz
Tyndall's Park Road, Bristol BS8 1PP
Tel: (0272) 741111
Phone-in: (0272) 238877
Weekend West Sat 9.40 a.m.
(fortnightly)
Ray Davey
The Good Taste Show Sun 9.30–
11.00 a.m.
Ray Davey

BBC RADIO CORNWALL
FM Mid & West 103.9 North & East
95.2 Sally 96

MW Mid & West 630 kHz North &
East 657 kHz
Phoenix Wharf, Truro TR1 1UA
Tel: (0872) 75421
Phone-in: (0872) 222222
Weekend Breakfast Sat 7.20 a.m.
David Pearce
Philip McMillan-Browse
Gardening Club Sun 12.30 p.m.
David Pearce
Philip McMillan-Browse
Jack Andrews

BBC RADIO DEVON
FM Exeter 95.8 Plymouth 103.4
N Devon 94.8 & 103.4
Torbay 103.4 Okehampton 96.0
MW Exeter 990 kHz Plymouth
855 kHz N Devon 801 kHz
Torbay 1485 kHz
PO Box 100 St David's Hill, Exeter
EX4 4DB
Tel: (0392) 215651
Phone-in: (0392) 269611
also
PO Box 5 Plymouth PL1 2AD
Tel: (0752) 260323
Phone-in: (0752) 269611
Good Morning Devon! Sun 8.40 a.m.
Dennis Cornish
Afternoon Show
Mon 3.10 p.m. Naila Green
Tues 3.30 p.m. Don Cookman
Fri 3.10 p.m. Ken Allen
(fortnightly)

BBC RADIO GLOUCESTER
FM 104.7 Stroud 95.0 Cirencester 95.8
London Road, Gloucester GL1 1SW
Tel: (0452) 308585
Phone-in: (0452) 307575
Mid-morning Show Thurs 11.30 a.m.
Reg Moule

BBC RADIO PLYMOUTH
for transmission and address details see
Radio Devon
Plymouth AM (fortnightly)
Dennis Cornish
Good Morning Devon!
see Radio Devon
Afternoon Show
see Radio Devon

BBC SOMERSET SOUND
MW 1323 kHz
14–16 Paul Street, Taunton TA1 3PF
Tel: (0823) 252437
Phone-in: (0823) 251641
Countywide Fri 3.10 p.m.
Vic Verrier
Phone-in alternate weeks

BBC WILTSHIRE SOUND
FM N Wilts 103.6 W Wilts 104.3
Salisbury 103.5
MW N Wilts: 1368 kHz
W Wilts 1323 kHz
PO Box 1234, Salisbury SP1 3DX
Tel: (0722) 411280
Phone-in: (0793) 513366
Wiltshire Today Wed 9.50 a.m.
Fred Friar
Graham Seaman Mon 2.30 p.m.
(fortnightly)
Don Cockman and Bert Hoare

SOUTH

BBC RADIO SOLENT
FM 96.1
MW 999 kHz Bournemouth 1359 kHz
Broadcasting House, Havelock Road,
Southampton SO1 OXR
Tel: (0703) 631311
Phone-in: (0703) 631316
Top Soil Sat 1.05–2.00 p.m.
Sarah Watts and team

Drivetime Show Mon 4.30 p.m.
Bill Boyd
Brian Kidd

RADIO SURREY
FM 104.6
Broadcasting House, Guildford
GU2 5AP
Tel: (0483) 306113
see Radio Sussex

BBC RADIO SUSSEX
FM C&S Sussex 95.3 E Sussex 104.5
N Sussex 104
MW C&S 1485 kHz E Sussex 1161 kHz
N Sussex 1368
Marlborough Place, Brighton
BN1 1TU
Tel: (0273) 680231
Phone-in (0273) 570057
Spare Time Sat 8.00 a.m.
Dave Fitton, Vic Kemp and Ashley
Stevenson
Miranda Birch Programme
Tues 2.10 p.m.
Charles Bowen
David on Sunday Sun 11.15 a.m.
Bert Winbourne

SOUTH EAST

BBC ESSEX
FM N&C Essex 103.5 S Essex 95.3
MW 765 kHz
PO Box 765, Chelmsford, Essex
CM2 9XB
Tel: (0245) 262393
Phone-in: (0245) 495050
Saturday Breakfast with Kara Tritton
7.45 a.m.
Ken Crowther
Down to Earth Sat 12.00–1.00 p.m.
Ken Crowther

BBC RADIO KENT
FM 96.7, 104.2
MW 1035, 1602, 774 kHz
Sun Pier, Chatham, Kent ME4 4EZ
Tel: (0634) 830505
Phone-in: (0634) 811111
also
20/22 Watting Street, Canterbury
CT1 2UL
Tel: (0227) 763063
Collard's Clinic Sun 7.00–8.00 a.m.
Bob Collard
Afternoon Show Tues 2.00–5.00 p.m.
(monthly)
Bob Collard

SOUTH CENTRAL

BBC RADIO BEDFORDSHIRE
FM S Beds, Herts, Bucks 103.8
N Bucks 104.5
N Beds, N Herts 95.5
MW Beds, Herts, Bucks 630 kHz
N Beds 1161 kHz
PO Box 476, Hastings Street, Luton,
LU1 5BA
Tel: (0582) 459111
Phone-in: (0582) 455555

Breakfast in Beds Sat
8.30–9.30 a.m.
Barry Timms
Susie Barnes Show 2.10 p.m. (monthly)
Geoffrey Farr

BBC RADIO BERKSHIRE
FM W Berks 104.1 E Berks 95.4
42a Portman Road, Reading RG3 1NB
Tel: (0734) 567056
Berkshire Network Fri 10.30 a.m.
(fortnightly)
Bill Partridge
Phil Rapps
see Radio Oxford
Bill Rennells
see Radio Oxford

BBC RADIO OXFORD
FM 95.2
MW 1485 kHz
269 Banbury Road, Oxford OX2 7DW
Tel: (0865) 311444
Phone-in: (0865) 311111
Phil Rapps Wed 3.30 p.m.
Ron Bateman
Bill Rennells Sun 9.30 a.m.
Ron Bateman

WEST

BBC RADIO SHROPSHIRE
FM 96.0 Ludlow 95.0
MW 75.6 kHz Ludlow 1584 kHz
PO Box 397, Shrewsbury SY1 3TT
Tel: (0743) 248484
Phone-in: (0743) 248321
The Gardening Programme Sat
1.00–2.00 p.m.
Angela Mansell
Martin Ford

MIDLANDS/ANGLIA

BBC RADIO CAMBRIDGESHIRE
FM 96.0
MW 1026 kHz
PO Box 96 Cambridge CB2 1LD
Tel: (0223) 315970
Phone-in: (0223) 315444
Andrew Wilson Sat 7.40 a.m.
Peter Jackson
Mandy Morton Wed 2.20 p.m.
Peter Jackson
Charles Patman

BBC RADIO CWR
FM Coventry & Warwick 94.8
FM Warwick, Leamington, Stratford &
S Warks 103.7
FM Nuneaton & Atherstone 104
25 Warwick Road, Coventry CV1 2WR
Tel: (0203) 559911
Phone-in: (0203) 231231
Steve Woodhall Thurs 3.00 p.m.
(monthly)
Ken Avery

BBC RADIO DERBY
FM 104.5, 94.2, 95.3
MW 1116 kHz
PO Box 269, Derby DE1 3HL
Tel: (0332) 361111
Phone-in: (0332) 616161
Graham Knight Fri 11.00 a.m.
David Griffiths
Martin Latimer

BBC RADIO LEICESTER
FM 104.9
MW 837 kHz
Epic House, Charles Street, Leicester
LE1 3SH
Tel: (0533) 516688
Phone-in: (0533) 422222
Down to Earth Sat 12.30 p.m. *repeated*
Sun 2.30 p.m.
Geoff Amos and guests

BBC RADIO LINCOLNSHIRE
FM 94.9
MW 1368 kHz
PO Box 219, Newport, Lincoln
LN1 3XY
Tel: (0522) 511411
Phone-in: (0522) 511219
Tea Time Every third Tues 4.15 p.m.
Simon Ellis

BBC RADIO NORFOLK
FM 95.1
MW E Norfolk 855 kHz W Norfolk
873 kHz
Norfolk Tower, Surrey Street, Norwich
NR1 3PA
Tel: (0603) 617411
Phone-in: (0603) 617321
Wally at the weekend Sat 12.00–
1.00 p.m. Sun 3.00 4.00 p.m.
Charles Henderson
Ray Loose
Carol Bundock Wed 11.15 a.m.
Charles Henderson
Ray Loose

BBC RADIO NORTHAMPTON
FM 104.2, 103.6
MW 1107 kHz
PO Box 1107, Abingdon Street,
Northampton NN1 2BE
Tel: (0604) 239100
Phone-in: (0604) 234455
Over the Garden Fence Sun
1.00–1.30 p.m.
Dave Watkins
Nicholas Warliker
John Bosworth
In Company Thurs 2.00–3.00 p.m.
(monthly)
Dave Watkins
Saturday Breakfast Show Sat 7.20 a.m.
Dave Watkins

BBC RADIO NOTTINGHAM
FM 103.8, 95.5
MW 1584 kHz
York House, Mansfield Road,
Nottingham NG1 3JB
Tel: (0602) 415161
Phone-in: (0602) 343434
Dave Simms Thurs 10.40 a.m.
(fortnightly)
John Stirland

BBC RADIO PETERBOROUGH
FM 95.7
MW 1449 kHz
PO Box 957, Peterborough PE1 1YT
Tel: (0733) 312832
Phone-in: (0733) 315444
Andrew Wilson
(*see* Radio Cambridge)
Mandy Morton
(*see* Radio Cambridge)

BBC RADIO STOKE
FM 94.6
MW 200 kHz
Cheapside, Hanley, Stoke-on-Trent
ST1 1JJ (0782) 208080
In the Potting Shed Sun 2.30 p.m.
repeated Tues 7.30 p.m.
Glyn Johnson

BBC RADIO SUFFOLK
FM E Suffolk 103.9 W Suffolk 104.6
Lowestoft 95.5
Broadcasting House, St Matthew's
Street, Ipswich IP1 3EP
Tel: (0473) 250000
Phone-in: (0473) 212121
Gardening Club Sat 8.00–9.00 a.m.
Ric Staines and guests
Suffolk Daily Wed, 10.00–11.00 a.m.
Roy Lacey

NORTH EAST

BBC RADIO CLEVELAND
FM 95.0 Whitby 95.8
MW 1548 kHz
PO Box 954B, Broadcasting House,
Newport Road, Middlesborough
TS1 5DG
Tel: (0642) 225211
Phone-in: (0642) 225511
Midmorning Thurs 10.15 a.m.
(fortnightly)
repeated on the *Mark Page Show* Sun
9.15 a.m.
Alan Delamore
Waynman Strike

BBC RADIO HUMBERSIDE
FM 95.9
MW 1485 kHz
9 Chapel Street, Hull HU1 3NU
Tel: (0482) 23232
Phone-in: (0482) 27744 from N of
Humber
Phone-in: (0472) 353501 from S of
Humber
Steve Massam Mon 2.15 p.m.
(fortnightly)
Dick Robinson

BBC RADIO LEEDS
FM 92.4, 95.3
MW 774 kHz
Broadcasting House, Woodhouse
Lane, Leeds LS2 9PN
Tel: (0532) 442131
Phone-in: (0532) 443222
Gardeners Direct Line Sat
7.00–8.00 a.m.
Philip Swindells
Joe Maiden
Jane Oland

BBC RADIO SHEFFIELD
FM Sheffield 88.6 Chesterfield 94.7
all other areas 104.1

MW 1035 kHz
Ashdell Grove, 60 Westbourne Road,
Sheffield SIO 2QU
Tel: (0742) 686185
Phone-in: (0742) 682682
Julie Mill's Sunday Show Sun
10.30 a.m.
Stuart Jackson
Morning Show Fri 12.00 p.m.
Jackie Eliot
Don Williams

BBC RADIO YORK
FM C 103.7 E 95.5 W & NW 104.3
MW C & E 1260 kHz W & NW
655 kHz
20 Bootham Row, York YO3 7BR
Tel: (0904) 641351
Phone-in: (0904) 641641
Saturday Breakfast Show Sat 8.35 a.m.
Roger Brooke, or
Ian Bentley

NORTH WEST

BBC RADIO CUMBRIA
FM N 95.6 W 95.6 S 96.1 Kendal 95.2
Windermere 104.2
MW N 756 kHz W 1458 kHz S 836 kHz
Hilltop Heights, London Road,
Carlisle CA1 2NA
Tel: (0228) 31661
Phone-in: (0228) 38484
Saturday Breakfast Show Sat 9.15 a.m.
Jeff Fullard
Paul O'Neill
Open Air Mon 12.00 p.m.
(fortnightly phone-in)
Henry Noblett

BBC RADIO LANCASHIRE
FM C&W 103.9 E 95.5 N 104.5
MW C&W&E 855 kHz N 1557 kHz
Darwen St, Blackburn BB2 2EA
Tel: (0254) 262411
Phone-in: (0254) 583583
Lancashire Garden Sun 1.05–2.00 p.m.
Judith Roberts
Lancashire Today Sat 6.50 a.m. and
8.50 a.m.
Robin Squance

BBC RADIO MERSEYSIDE
FM 95.8
MW 1485 kHz
55 Paradise St, Liverpool L1 3BP
Tel: (051) 709 9333
Linda Mac! Fri 1.30 p.m.
Eric Hardy

IRELAND

BBC RADIO ULSTER
FM 92.4–95.4
MW 1341 kHz Enniskillen 873 kHz
Broadcasting House, Ormeau Avenue,
Belfast BT2 8HQ
Tel: (0232) 338000
Phone-in: (0232) 325757
Gardeners Corner Sat 9.05–10 a.m.
Libby Hunter

WALES

BBC RADIO CLWYD
FM 97.1, 103.4
MW 1260 kHz
AM 657 kHz
The Old School House, Glanrafon
Road, Mold CH7 1PA
Tel: (0352) 700367
Phone-in: (0352) 700367
Roundabout Mon 9.45 a.m.
(fortnightly)
Alan Daulby
Olive Sweetman

BBC RADIO CYMRU
FM 92.4–94.6, 96.8 & 103.5–105
BBC Bryn Meirion, Meirion Road,
Bangor, Gwynedd LL57 2BY
Tel: (0248) 370880
Garddio Every third Sun 2.00–
2.30 p.m. *repeated* Fri 6.00 p.m.
Dei Tomos

BBC RADIO WALES
AM 882 kHz
Broadcasting House, Llandaff, Cardiff
CF5 2YQ
Tel: (0222) 572888
See *Radio Times* for details

SCOTLAND

BBC RADIO SCOTLAND
FM 92.4
MW 810 kHz
5 Queen Street, Edinburgh EH2 1JF
Tel: (031) 225 3131
Down to Earth Thurs 1.30 p.m.
repeated 7.02 p.m. MW
Lesley Watson
Adam Martin

BBC RADIO SOLWAY
MW 585 kHz
Elmbank, Lover's Walk, Dumfries
DG1 1NZ
Tel: (0387) 68008
Country Matters Tues 12.00 p.m.
(fortnightly)
Brian Ross
Alistair Bertram

BBC RADIO TWEED
FM 93.5
Municipal Buildings, High Street,
Selkirk IO7 4BU
Tel: (0750) 21884
Landscape Mon 5.30–6.00 p.m.
(monthly)
Dan Buglass
Clare Colebrook

Organizations

Trade organizations are mainly concerned with assisting their members in several ways, but can also be a source of useful information for gardeners. Generally, they'll be the administrators of a code of conduct which controls the quality and service expected from members. If, for example, you're thinking of having your garden landscaped, you'd be very well advised to use a member of the British Association of Landscape Industries from whom you can expect a decent job. And if, by any chance, you don't get it, well you can complain to the Association who will take action.

Other organizations too will be happy to give you advice concerning their particular speciality. You may fear problems over the security of your allotment site. In that case the National Society of Allotment and Leisure Gardeners will be able to help. If you think you've bred a winning rose, then the British Rose Growers Association may want to hear, while a complaint about bad John Innes compost should be directed at the John Innes Compost Manufacturers Association.

Official Organizations

Arboricultural Association
Ampfield House, Ampfield, Romsey, Hampshire SO51 9PA

Botanical Gardens Conservation Secretariat
Descanso House, 199 Kew Road, Richmond, Surrey TW9 3BW

Botanical Society of the British Isles
c/o Dept of Botany, The Natural History Museum, Cromwell Road, London SW7 5BD

British Agricultural & Garden Machinery Association
14/16 Church Street, Rickmansworth, Hertfordshire WD3 1RQ

British Agrochemicals Association Ltd
4 Lincoln Court, Lincoln Road, Peterborough PE1 2RP

British Association of Landscape Industries (BALI)
Landscape House, 9 Henry Street, Keighley, West Yorkshire BD21 3DR

British Association of Rose Breeders
6 New Road, North Runcton, King's Lynn, Norfolk PE33 ORA

British Bedding Plant Association
c/o NFU Horticulture Department, Agriculture House, Knightsbridge, London SW1X 7NJ

British Bonsai Association
J White, 36 McCarthy Way, Wokingham, Berkshire RG11 4UA

British Dahlia Growers Association
c/o Halls of Heddon, West Heddon Nurseries, Heddon on the Wall, Newcastle upon Tyne NE15 OJS

British Orchid Council
A J Hainsworth, 52 Weaste Lane, Thelwell, Cheshire WA4 3JR

British Rose Growers Association
90 Derby Road, Risley, Derbyshire DE7 3SU

British Trust for Ornithology
The Nunnery, Nunnery Place, Thetford, Norfolk IP24 2PU

Bulb Information Desk
43 King Street, London WC2E 8RJ

Council for the Protection of Rural England
Warwick House, 25 Buckingham Palace Road, London SW1W 0PP

Department of the Environment
2 Marsham Street, London SW1

English Vineyards Association
38 West Park, London SE0 4RH

Federation to Promote Horticulture for the Disabled
252 The Ridgeway, Enfield, Middlesex EN2 8AP

Fertiliser Manufacturers Association
Greenhill House, Thorpe Wood, Peterborough PE3 6GF

Forestry Commission
231 Corstorphine Road, Edinburgh EH12 7AT

Fruit Group of the RHS
Mrs M Sweetingham, RHS, Vincent Square, London SW1P 2PE

Garden History Society
5 The Knoll, Hereford HR1 1RU

The Gardener's Royal Benevolent Society
Bridge House, 139 Kingston Road, Leatherhead, Surrey KT22 7NT

Gardens for Disabled Trust
Hayes Farm House, Hayes Lane, Peasmarsh, East Sussex TN31 6XR

Good Gardeners Association
Two Mile Lane, Highnam, Gloucester GL2 8DW

Health & Safety Executive
St Hughes House (Room 414), Trinity Road, Stanley Precinct Bootle, Merseyside L20 3QY

Henry Doubleday Research Association
National Centre For Organic Gardening, Ryton on Dunsmore, Coventry, West Midlands CV8 3LG
see also page 000

Horticultural Therapy
Goulds Ground, Vallis Way, Frome, Somerset BA11 3DW

Horticultural Trades Association
Horticultural House, 19 High Street, Theale, Reading, Berkshire RG7 5AH

Horticulture Research International
Wellesbourne, Warwickshire CV35 9EF

Institute of Groundmanship
19–23 Church Street, The Agora,
Wolverton, Buckinghamshire
MK12 5LG

The Institute of Horticulture
PO Box 313, 80 Vincent Square,
London SW1P 2PE

**Institute of Leisure & Amenity
Management**
Lower Basildon, Reading, Berkshire
RG8 9NE

International Bee Research Society
18 North Road, Cardiff CF1 3DY

International Plant Propagators Society
Mears Ashby Nurseries, Glebe House,
Glebe Road, Mears Ashby,
Northampton NN6 0DL

John Innes Manufacturers Association
c/o Joseph Bentley Ltd, Back Lane,
Barrow on Humber, South
Humberside DN19 7AQ

Joint Council for Landscape Industries
Landscape House, 9 Henry Street,
Keighley, West Yorkshire BD21 3DR

The Landscape Institute
6/7 Barnard Mews, London SW11 1QU
See also page 000

**London Association of Recreational
Gardeners**
45 The Ridgeway, Kenton, Harrow,
Middlesex HA3 0LN

The Men of the Trees
Sandy Lane, Crawley Down, West
Sussex RH10 4HS

**Ministry of Agriculture, Fisheries &
Food (MAFF)**
(Pesticides Safety Division),
Rothamsted, Harpenden,
Hertfordshire AL5 2SS

Mushroom Growers Association
2 St Paul's Street, Stamford,
Lincolnshire PE9 2BE

**National Association of Flower
Arrangement Societies of Great Britain**
21 Denbigh Street, London SW1 2HF

**National Council for the Conservation
of Plants and Gardens**
The Pines, Wisley Gardens, Woking,
Surrey GU23 6QB

National Gardens Scheme
Hatchlands Park, East Clandon,
Guildford, Surrey GU4 7RT

National Institute of Medical Herbalists
9 Palace Gate, Exeter, Devon
EX1 1JA

**National Institute of Agricultural
Botany**
Huntingdon Road, Cambridge
CB3 0LE

**National Society of Allotment & Leisure
Gardeners**
Hunters Road, Corby,
Northamptonshire NN17 1JE

The National Trust
36 Queen Anne's Gate, London
SW1H 9AS

National Trust for Scotland
Gardening Advice Centre, Greenbank
House, Clarkston, Glasgow G76 8RB

Northern Horticultural Society
Harlow Carr Botanical Gardens, Crag
Lane, Harrogate, North Yorkshire
HG3 1QB

Nuffield Orthopedic Centre NHS Trust
Windmill Road, Headington, Oxford
OX3 7LD

Organic Growers Association
86 Colston Street, Bristol, Avon
BS1 5BB

Plant Variety Rights Office
White House Lane, Huntingdon Road,
Cambridge CB3 0LF

Professional Gardeners Guild
Oak House, Sutton Park, Sutton
Green, Nr Guildford, Surrey
GU4 7QN

Royal Caledonian Horticultural Society
2 Buckstone Way, Edinburgh
EH10 6PN

**Royal Forestry Society of England,
Wales & Northern Ireland**
102 High Street, Tring, Hertfordshire
SG4 8UT

Royal Gardener's Orphan Fund
48 St Albans Road, Codicote, Hitchin,
Hertfordshire SG4 8UT

Royal Horticultural Society
80 Vincent Square, London SW1P 2PE

Royal Horticultural Society of Ireland
Swanbrook House, Bloomfield
Avenue, Donnybrook, Dublin 4, Eire

Royal Horticultural Society's Garden
Wisley, Woking, Surrey GU23 6QB

Royal Society for Protection of Birds
The Lodge, Sandy, Bedfordshire
SG19 2DL

Scotland's Garden Scheme
31 Castle Terrace, Edinburgh
EH1 2EL

Society of Floristry
The Old Schoolhouse, Payford,
Redmarley, Gloucestershire
GL19 3HY

Society of Garden Designers
23 Reigate Road, Ewell, Surrey
KT17 1PS

Soil Association
86 Colston Street, Bristol BS1 5BB

**Somerset Trust for Nature
Conservation**
Fyne Court, Broomfield, Bridgwater,
Somerset TA5 2EQ

Sports Turf Research Institute
Bingley, West Yorkshire BD16 1AU

The Tradescant Trust
Museum of Garden History, St-Mary-
at-Lambeth, Lambeth Palace Road,
London SE1 7JU

Tree Council
35 Belgrave Square, London
SW1X 8QN

The Tree Register of the British Isles
Tilgates, Bletchingley, Surrey
RH1 4QF

Women's Farm & Garden Association
175 Gloucester Street, Cirencester,
Gloucestershire GL7 2DP

Woodland Trust
Autumn Park, Dysart Road,
Grantham, Lincolnshire NG31 6LL

The Worshipful Company of Gardeners
25 Luke Street, London EC2A 4AR

Societies

As gardeners' interests in plants grow, they often become hooked on one particular group of plants. I've met alpine enthusiasts for whom the plant world starts at about ten thousand feet, and there are gardeners whose gardens grow nothing at all but ferns, and the fuchsia enthusiasts who – well, need I go on?

There are also much more general societies like the Hardy Plant Society, the Cottage Garden Society and, of course, the Royal Horticultural Society. I belong to all three of those and look forward greatly to their monthly or quarterly bulletins and the many events they stage.

But perhaps the greatest advantage of joining a society is that, without exception, they are filled with gardeners who have unrivalled specialist knowledge which they're eager to share with fellow enthusiasts. You'll learn a lot by joining one and you'll make a lot of new friends too.

Specialist Societies

Alpine Garden Society
AGS Centre, Avon Bank, Pershore,
Worcestershire WR10 3JP

British & European Geranium Society
85 Sparrow Farm Road, Ewell, Surrey
KT17 2LP

British Bonsai Association
Daisy Cottage, 131 Nine Mile Ride,
Wokingham RG11 4HY

British Cactus & Succulent Society
43 Dewar Drive, Sheffield, South
Yorkshire S7 2GR

British Clematis Society
115 Belmont Road, Harrow, Middlesex
HA3 7PL

The British Fuchsia Society
20 Brodawel, Llannon, Dyfed
SA14 6BJ

British Geranium Society
56 Shringley Road, Higher Poynton,
Cheshire SK12 1TF

British Gladiolus Society
4 Meadow View, Skelmanthorpe,
Huddersfield, West Yorkshire
HD8 9ET

British Hosta & Hemerocallis Society
Cleave House, Sticklepath,
Okehampton, Devon EX20 2NN

British Iris Society
43 Sea Lane, Goring by Sea, West Sussex BN12 4QD

British Ivy Society
14 Holly Grove, Huyton, Merseyside L36 4JA

British National Carnation Society
3 Canberra Close, Hornchurch, Essex RM12 5TR

The British Orchid Growers Association
c/o McBeans Orchids, Cooksbridge, Lewes, Sussex BN8 4PR

British Pelargonium & Geranium Society
134 Montrose Avenue, Welling, Kent DA16 2QY

British Pteridological (Fern) Society
'Croziers', 16 Kirby Corner Road, Canley, Coventry, West Midlands CV4 8GD

Carnivorous Plant Society
174 Baldwins Lane, Croxley Green, Hertfordshire WD3 3LQ

Cottage Garden Society
5 Nixon Close, Thornhill, Dewsbury, West Yorkshire WF12 0JA

Cyclamen Society
Tile Barn House, Standen Street, Iden Green, Benenden, Kent TN17 4LB

Daffodil Society
32 Montgomery Avenue, Sheffield, South Yorkshire S7 1NZ

Delphinium Society
143 Victoria Road, Horley, Surrey RH6 7AS

European Bromeliad Society
16 Culcheth Hall Drive, Culcheth, Warrington, Cheshire WA3 4PS

European Geranium Society
56 Shringley Road, Higher Poynton, Cheshire SK12 1TF

Ferns *see* **British Pteridological Society**

Fruit Group of the Royal Horticultural Society
RHS, 80 Vincent Square, London SW1P 2PE

Garden History Society
5 The Knoll, Hereford HR1 1RU

Hardy Plant Society
Bank Cottage, Great Comberton, Nr Pershore, Worcestershire WR10 3DP

Heather Society
Denbeigh, All Saints Road, Creeting St Mary, Ipswich, Suffolk IP6 8PJ

Hebe Society
Rosemergy, Hain Walk, St Ives, Cornwall TR26 2AF

The Herb Society
PO Box 415, London SW1P 2HE

International Camellia Society
41 Galveston Road, East Putney, London SW15 2RZ

International Clematis Society
(Europe and Overseas Branch), 3 La Route du Coude, Rocquaine, St Pierre du Bois, Guernsey, Channel Islands

International Clematis Society
The Tropical Bird Gardens, Rode, Nr Bath, Somerset BA3 6QW

International Dendrology Society
School House, Stannington, Morpeth, Northumberland NE61 6HF

International Water Lily Society
Rose Farm, 19 Putton Lane, Chickerell, Weymouth, Dorset DT3 4AF

Irish Garden Plant Society
c/o National Botanic Gardens,
Glasnevin, Dublin 9, Eire

Lily Group of the Royal Horticultural Society
14 Marshalls Way, Wheathampstead,
St Albans, Hertfordshire AL4 8HY

Mammillaria Society
26 Glenfield Road, Banstead, Surrey
SM7 2DG

National Auricula & Primula Society
(Southern Section), 67 Warnham Court
Road, Carshalton Beeches, Surrey
SM5 3ND

National Auricula & Primula Society
(Midland & West Section), 6 Lawson
Close, Saltford, Bristol, Avon
BS18 3LB

National Auricula & Primula Society
(Northern Section), 146 Queens Road,
Cheadle Hulme, Cheshire SK8 5HY

National Begonia Society
7 Springwood Close, Thurgoland,
Sheffield, South Yorkshire S30 7AB

National Bonsai Society
24 Bidston Road, Liverpool L4 7XJ

National Chrysanthemum Society
2 Lucas House, Craven Road, Rugby
CV21 3HY

National Dahlia Society
19 Sunnybank, Marlow,
Buckinghamshire SL7 3BL

National Pot Leek Society
23 Beanley Place, High Heaton,
Newcastle upon Tyne NE7 7DQ

National Sweet Pea Society
3 Chalk Farm Road, Stokenchurch,
Buckinghamshire HP14 3TB

National Vegetable Society
56 Waun-y-Groes Avenue, Rhiwbini,
Cardiff, South Glamorgan CF4 4SZ

National Vegetable Society
(Southern Branch), 94 Heathfield
Avenue, Dover, Kent CT16 2PD

National Vegetable Society
(Midland Branch), 8 Halton Street,
Netherton, Dudley, West Midlands
DY2 OPJ

National Vegetable Society
(Northern Branch), 33 Newmarket
Road, Redcar, Cleveland TS10 2HY

National Vegetable Society
(Scottish Branch), Rose Cottage, 74
Strathaven Road, Kirkmuirhill
ML11 9RW

National Viola & Pansy Society
28 Carisbrook Road, Edgbaston,
Birmingham B17 8NW

Northern Horticultural Society
Harlow Carr Botanical Gardens, Crag
Lane, Harrogate, North Yorkshire
HG3 1QB

North of England Rose, Carnation and Sweet Pea Society
94 Hedgehope Road, Westerhope,
Newcastle upon Tyne NE5 4LA

Orchid Society of Great Britain
120 Crofton Road, Orpington, Kent
BR6 8HZ

Royal Caledonian Horticultural Society
2 Buckstone Way, Edinburgh
EH10 6PN

Royal Horticultural Society
See Organizations (p. 19)

Royal Horticultural Society's Garden
See Organizations (p. 19)

Royal National Rose Society
Chiswell Green, St Albans,
Hertfordshire AL2 3NR

Saintpaulia & Houseplant Society
33 Church Road, Newbury Park,
Ilford, Essex IG2 7ET

Scottish Begonia Society
126 Sheephousehill, Fauldhouse,
Bathgate, West Lothian EH47 9EL

Scottish Gladiolus Society
63 Gardiner Road, Blackhall,
Edinburgh EH4 3RL

**Scottish National Sweet Pea, Rose &
Carnation Society**
72 West George Street, Coatbridge,
Lanarkshire ML5 2DD

Scottish Rock Garden Club
21 Merchiston Park, Edinburgh
EH10 4PW

The Sempervivum Society
11 Wingle Tye Road, Burgess Hill,
West Sussex RH15 9HR

**Tulip Society of Wakefield & Northern
England**
70 Wrenthorpe Lane, Wrenthorpe,
Wakefield, West Yorkshire WF2 OPT

Wild Flower Society
68 Outwoods Road, Loughborough,
Leicestershire LE11 3LY

Allotment Gardeners

**The National Society of Allotment and
Leisure Gardeners Limited**
Registered Office:
Hunters Road, Corby,
Northamptonshire NN17 1JE
Tel: (0536) 66576

MANAGEMENT COMMITTEE
REGIONAL REPRESENTATIVES
East Midlands
Mr H E Todd
4 Norfolk Close, Corby,
Northamptonshire NN17 2ZL

Eastern
Mr J Farmer
11 Ivel Way, Flitwick, Bedfordshire
MK45 1ER

North West
Mr H S Ridehalgh
379 Blackburn Road, West End,
Oswaldtwistle, Lancashire BB5 4NA

Northern
Mr J J Austin Davis
13 Byron Avenue, Blackhall Colliery,
Hartlepool, Cleveland TS27 4NG

South East
Mrs J Gay
28 Rochester Avenue, Rochester Upon
Medway, Kent ME1 2DW

South West
Mr S J Hartree
3 Sandford Road, Weston-Super-Mare,
Avon BS23 3EX

Southern
Mr D Parsons, 59 Devizes Road,
Salisbury, Wiltshire SP2 7LQ

Welsh Region
Mr A Rees
36 Lansbury Crescent, Maesteg, Mid
Glamorgan CF34 9LY

West Midlands
Mr G Kirby
12 Deans Way, Exhall, Coventry, West
Midlands, CV7 9HD

Yorkshire
Mr D J Humphreys
'Staveley', Spring Hall Lane, Halifax,
Yorkshire HX1 4JE

Organic Gardeners

Henry Doubleday Research Association (HDRA)
National Centre for Organic Gardening
Ryton on Dunsmore
Coventry CV8 3LG
Tel: (0203) 303517

LOCAL CLUBS AFFILIATED TO HDRA

Avon Organic Group
c/o Mr J Lucas (Secretary)
33 Daisy Road, Greenbank, Bristol,
Avon BS5 6JS

Bath Organic Group
c/o Mrs V Phillips
7 New Road, Bradford-on-Avon,
Wiltshire BA15 1AR

Bentham Organic Gardening Group
c/o Jo Taylor
Close House, Low Bentham, Lancaster
LA2 7DG

Berkshire Organic Gardeners
c/o Dr Peggy Ellis
64 Blenheim Road, Caversham,
Reading, Berkshire RG4 7RS

Braintree Organic Gardening Club
c/o A Pudney
13 Woodfield Road, Braintree, Essex
CM7 6HZ

Brighton & Lewis Organic Gardening Group
c/o Mrs E F Robinson
27B Clifton Road, Brighton, East
Sussex BN1 3HN

Buckinghamshire Organic Gardeners (South)
c/o Mrs J Edmonds
10 Woodwat, Beaconsfield,
Buckinghamshire HP9 1DH

Calder Valley Organic Gardeners
c/o Mr K Williams
1 Regent Street, Hebden Bridge, West
Yorkshire HX4 7DG

Cardiff Organic Gardeners
c/o Mrs Margaret Foster
82 Lakeside Drive, Cardiff CF2 6DG

Cheshire Organic Group (East)
c/o Mrs L Mountain
19 Benbrook Way, Gawsworth,
Macclesfield, Cheshire SK11 9RT

Chilterns & Oxfordshire Organic Group
c/o Mr D Francis
12 Harts Road, Haddenham,
Aylesbury, Buckinghamshire
HP17 8HJ

Colchester Green Network Organic Gardening Group
c/o Mrs Vera Chaney
9 Clairmont Road, Lexden,
Colchester, Essex CO3 5BE

Cornish Group
c/o Mrs J W Moore
Sunnyside Farm, Goonhavern, Truro,
Cornwall TR4 9JG

Cumbria Organic Gardeners & Farmers
c/o J Symons (Honorary Secretary)
10 Brackenber Lodge, Shap, Penrith
CA10 3QB

Derbyshire Organic Growers
c/o Wendy Hughes
Windhaven, 1 Derwent Terrace, Old
Hackney Lane, Hackney, Matlock
DE4 2QL

Devon Organic Gardeners (South)
c/o Mr D P Hathaway
4A Berry Meadow, Kingsteignton,
Newton Abbot, Devon TQ12 5AL

**Dumfries & Galloway Organic
Association**
c/o Ms Sarah Eno
Bankend, Lauriston, Castle Douglas
DG7 2PW

Exeter Organic Gardening Group
c/o Mr W Branney
South Lodge, Columbjohn, Rewe,
Devon EX5 4ER

The Findhorn Foundation
Isle of Erraid
Fionnphort, Isle of Mull, Argyll
PA66 6BN

Forth Valley Organic Association
c/o Ms Ingrid Robson
Dalbrack Cottage, Kilbryde,
Dunblane, Perthshire FK15 9NF

Hampshire Group
c/o Mrs D Wright (Honorary
Secretary)
Larks Barrow Market Garden,
Kingsclere Road, Whitchurch,
Hampshire RG28 7QB

Hampshire Self Sufficient Group (East)
c/o Mr A Fry (Honorary President)
Heather Cottage, Liss, Hampshire
GU33 7DD

Heart of England Organic Group
c/o Mr S Hammett (Honorary
Secretary)
Gate Farm, Fen End, Kenilworth,
Warwickshire CV8 1NW

Hertfordshire Organic Gardeners
c/o Mr M Gibbs
13 Cottonmill Crescent, St Albans,
Hertfordshire AL1 1HW

Horsham Organic Growers Society
c/o Mrs J Hardy (Secretary)
59 Amberley Road, Horsham, West
Sussex RH12 4LJ

**Hull & East Riding Organic Gardening
Association**
c/o S Connolly
19 Church Lane, Kirk Ella, Hull
HU10 7TA

Ipswich Organic Gardeners Group
c/o Mrs P Smith (Secretary)
23 Linsfiel, Rushnore St Andrew,
Ipswich IP5 7BA

Lakeland Organic Gardeners (South)
c/o Mr M Cook (Secretary)
72 Hollow Lane, Barrow-in-Furness,
Cumbria LA13 9HY

Leicester Organic Group
c/o Mr R Haskins
33 Piper Drive, Long Whatton,
Loughborough LE12 5DJ

Liverpool Organic Gardeners
c/o Mrs P Green
18 Court Hey Road, Liverpool
L16 2CZ

Llandysul Organic Gardening Club
c/o Mrs C S Beer
Bercoed Isaf, Pentrecernt, Llandysul
SA44 5BE

London (East) Organic Group
c/o Mr Roger Blackhouse
112 Thorold Road, Ilford, Essex
IG1 4EY

**London (South) Organic Gardeners
Group**
c/o Mrs Andria McGarth
18 Malvern Road, Surbiton, Surrey
KT6 7UQ

Luton Organic Group
c/o Mr Adam Pinney
74 Dane Road, Luton, Bedfordshire
LO3 1JP

Manchester Organic Gardeners
c/o Mrs J G Lloyd
22 Church Lane, Wrightington Bar,
Wigan WN6 9SL

Norfolk Group
c/o R R Gladden, (Honorary
Secretary)
159 Hall Street, Bristol, Melton
Constable NR24 2LQ

North East Branch
c/o Dr L F Marshall
10 Wallace Terrace, Ryton, Tyne &
Wear NE40 3PL

Pendle Organic Gardeners
c/o V Thome (Secretary)
154 Regent Street, Nelson, Lancashire
BB9 8SG

Penwith Organic Gardeners & Growers
c/o Y Lewer
The Old Chapel, Sithney, Helston,
Cornwall TR13 ORN

Romsey Organic Group
c/o B Jones (Secretary)
Fairhaven, Danes Road, Awbridge,
Romsey, Hampshire, SO51 0HL

Shropshire Organic Gardeners
c/o K Westgate
2 Manor Farm, Hordley, Ellesmere
SY12 9BB

Southwell Ecology Group
c/o Mrs G H Edwards
Clyde House, Westgate, Southwell
NG25 0JN

Suffolk Group
c/o Mr H W Case
Ladywell, Westhorpe, Stowmarket
IP14 4TQ

Tayside Organic Group
c/o Mrs J Menhinick
Muiredge Cottage, Errol, Perth
PH2 7RD

Warrington Organic & Wildlife Society
c/o Mr G Pilkington
1 Banbury Drive, Great Sankey,
Warrington, Cheshire WA5 1HW

Wiltshire Group (South)
c/o S Creasey
Best's Cottage, Farley, Salisbury,
Wiltshire SP5 1AY

Wirral Organic Group
c/o Mrs S C Tew
21 Monmouth Road, Wallasey, Wirral
L44 3EA

Yorkshire Dales Organic Gardeners
c/o Ms Judith Sutcliffe
Riddings, West Burton, Leyburn,
North Yorkshire DL8 4LG

Yorkshire Group (South)
c/o Ms L Rowley
690 Gleadless Road, Sheffield, South
Yorkshire S14 1LS

Horticultural Courses

If you're really interested in horticulture, at whatever level, there are great opportunities for learning more. If you just want to become a more successful amateur gardener, enrol for evening classes which are available in most areas.

If you, or one of your family, wish to make horticulture your career then you must decide first of all at which level you think you'll be successful, and which will suit your aspirations most.

There are plenty of courses to suit those people who would prefer to work with their hands, from the National Vocational Qualifications courses right up to the Advanced National Certificate.

Should you prefer a management qualification, you will find plenty of opportunities at several levels in the National Diploma, Higher National Diploma and degree courses. If it's a research career you're after, start by checking out the degree courses.

All colleges are keen to have candidates with the necessary qualifications and you'll find them extremely helpful. Just drop them a line detailing your requirements.

Information about part-time, evening, and day-release courses can be obtained from libraries, schools and colleges and local newspapers.

Information available at the library is dependent on that received from schools and colleges, therefore smaller libraries may not hold a vast amount of information. Main libraries also hold a *Directory of Further Education* which contains names and addresses of colleges which can be contacted for further details.

Schools and colleges generally publish a prospectus for courses commencing in September or October of each year, some of which are distributed locally through your door.

The local press may also advertise forthcoming courses at schools and colleges within your area.

The list at the end of this chapter includes the addresses of the main universities and colleges. The symbol * indicates those colleges which are also running a wide range of part-time courses on a day-release, block-release or evening basis.

Abbreviations used are as follows:

ANC	Advanced National Certificate (1 year)	NC	National Certificate (1 year)
ANCH	Advanced National Certificate in Horticulture (SCOTVEC) (1 year)	NCH	National Certificate in Horticulture (1 year)
		ND	National Diploma (3 year sandwich course)
BTEC	Business and Technical Education Council	NDH	National Diploma in Horticulture (3 year sandwich course)
First D	First Diploma (1 year)		
First DH	First Diploma in Horticulture (1 year)	NVQ	National Vocational Qualification (3 year day release course)
HND	Higher National Diploma (3 year sandwich course)		
HNDH	Higher National Diploma in Horticulture (3 year sandwich course)	SCOTVEC	Scottish Vocational Educational Council (equivalent to BTEC)

Royal Horticultural Society

Centres offering courses leading to the
RHS General Examination in
Horticulture:

England

AVON
Norton Radstock Technical College
Bristol University Botanic Garden

BERKSHIRE
Berkshire College of Agriculture

BUCKINGHAMSHIRE
Aylesbury College

CAMBRIDGESHIRE
Cambridgeshire Farm College
The Oundle Area Adult Education
   Centre

CHESHIRE
Cheshire College of Agriculture

CLEVELAND
Guisborough Agricultural Centre
Stockton/Billingham Technical
   College

CORNWALL
Duchy College of Agriculture &
   Horticulture

CUMBRIA
Cumbria College of Agriculture &
   Horticulture

DORSET
Dorset College of Agriculture

DURHAM
Durham College of Agriculture &
   Horticulture

EAST SUSSEX
Brighton College of Technology
Plumpton Agricultural College

ESSEX
Southend Adult Education Centre

GLOUCESTERSHIRE
Hartpury College

GREATER MANCHESTER
South Manchester College
Tameside College of Technology

HAMPSHIRE
Farnborough College of Technology

HERTFORDSHIRE
Cassio College

ISLE OF WIGHT
Isle of Wight College of Arts &
Technology

KENT
Hadlow College

LANCASHIRE
Lancashire College of Agriculture &
Horticulture

LEICESTERSHIRE
Brooksby College

LINCOLNSHIRE
Lincolnshire College of Agriculture &
Horticulture
Riseholme Hall

LONDON
Hampstead Garden Suburb Adult
Education Centre
Merton Institute of Adult Education
Sheen School
South London College
Southwark College
See also Middlesex and Surrey

MERSEYSIDE
Hughbard College
The Kennels Horticultural Centre

MIDDLESEX
Capel Manor College
Frays Adult Education Centre
Northwood Methodist Church Hall
Norwood Hall Institute of
Horticultural Education
Rooks Heath High School
Weald College
Whitton School

NORFOLK
Norfolk College of Agriculture &
Horticulture

NORTH HUMBERSIDE
Bishop Burton College of
Agriculture

NORTH YORKSHIRE
Northern Horticultural Society
Scarborough Technical College

NORTHAMPTONSHIRE
Moulton College
See also Cambridgeshire

NORTHUMBERLAND
Kirkley Hall College

NOTTINGHAMSHIRE
Brackenhurst College

OXFORDSHIRE
Oxfordshire County Teaching Farm

SHROPSHIRE
Grove School
Walford College of Agriculture

SOMERSET
Cannington College
Yeovil College

SOUTH YORKSHIRE
Barnsley College of Technology
Parsons Cross College
Rothervalley College of Further
  Education

SUFFOLK
Otley College of Agriculture &
  Horticulture

SURREY
Coulsdon Centre
See also London, Hampshire &
  Middlesex

WARWICKSHIRE
North Warwickshire College of
  Technology & Art
South Warwickshire College of
  Further Education
See also West Midlands

WEST MIDLANDS
Solihull College of Technology
Stourbridge College
Tile Hill College of Further
  Education
See also Warwickshire

WEST SUSSEX
Brinsbury College of Agriculture &
  Horticulture

WEST YORKSHIRE
Dewsbury College (Cleckheaton
  Centre)
Leeds Metropolitan University
Ralph Thoresby High School (Adult
  Education)
Shipley College
Wakefield District College
  (Hemsworth Centre)
West Park Evening Centre

WILTSHIRE
Lackham College of Agriculture

Wales

Afan College
Pencoed College

Scotland

The Barony College
Langside College
Threave School of Gardening

Channel Islands

Highlands College

Eire

Kildalton Agricultural &
  Horticultural College
National Botanic Gardens
Scoil Stiofain

National Vocational Qualification

Centres offering courses leading to
NVQ Phases I and II in Horticulture
(these replaced City and Guilds phases
I and II in September 1992. City &
Guilds phases III and IV remain the
same).

Entry requirements: A general interest
in gardening

England

AVON
Blaise Training Centre
Norton Radstock Technical College
Bristol Adult Education Area

BEDFORDSHIRE
The Further Education Centre
Shuttleworth College

BERKSHIRE
Berkshire College of Agriculture

CAMBRIDGESHIRE
Cambridgeshire County Farm
   College

CHESHIRE
Cheshire College of Agriculture
North Cheshire College

CORNWALL
Cornwall College of Further Education
   & Higher Education

CUMBRIA
Cumbria College of Agriculture &
   Forestry

DERBYSHIRE
Derbyshire College of Agriculture &
   Horticulture

DEVON
Bicton College of Agriculture
Dartington Hall Trust
St Loye's College

DORSET
Dorset College of Agriculture

DURHAM
Durham College of Agriculture &
   Horticulture
Finchale Training College

EAST SUSSEX
Brighton College of Technology
Plumpton Agricultural College

ESSEX
Barking College of Technology
Writtle Agricultural College

GLOUCESTERSHIRE
Gloucestershire College of
   Agriculture & Horticulture
The National Star Centre College of
   Further Education

GREATER MANCHESTER
South Manchester Community College
See also under Lancashire

HAMPSHIRE
Highbury College of Technology
Sparsholt College

HEREFORD & WORCESTER
Hereford College of Agriculture
Pershore College of Horticulture
Wyevale Training Group

HERTFORDSHIRE
Capel Manor Horticultural &
   Environmental Centre
Hertfordshire College of Agriculture
   & Horticulture

HUMBERSIDE
Bishop Burton College of Agriculture

ISLE OF WIGHT
Isle of Wight College of Arts &
   Technology

KENT
Canterbury College of Technology
Hadlow College of Agriculture &
   Horticulture
Mid Kent College of Higher &
   Further Education

LANCASHIRE
Blackpool and Fylde College of
   Further & Higher Education
Bolton Metropolitan College
Burnley College
Lancashire College of Agriculture &
   Horticulture
Lancashire College of Technology
Tameside College of Technology

Wigan College of Technology
See also Greater Manchester

LEICESTERSHIRE
Brooksby Agricultural College
Coalville College

LINCOLNSHIRE
Boston College of Further Education
Lincolnshire College of Agriculture
   & Horticulture

LONDON
Camden Training Centre
Royal Parks Division Training Centre
South London College
Southwark College
See also Middlesex and Surrey

MERSEYSIDE
Knowsley Central Tertiary College
Merseyside Parks Training Centre
St Helens College
St Helens College of Technology
South Mersey College
Southport College of Art &
   Technology
The Hugh Baird College of
   Technology
Wirral Metropolitan College

MIDDLESEX
Norwood Hall Institute of
   Horticultural Education
Richmond Upon Thames College

NORFOLK
Norfolk College of Agriculture

NORTH YORKSHIRE
Askham Bryan College
Craven College of Adult Education
Northern Horticultural Society

NORTHAMPTONSHIRE
Northamptonshire College of
   Agriculture

NORTHUMBERLAND
Northumberland College of
   Agriculture

NOTTINGHAMSHIRE
Nottinghamshire College of
   Agriculture
Portland Training College

SHROPSHIRE
Shropshire College of Further
   Education
Walford College of Agriculture

SOMERSET
Cannington College
The School of Agriculture and
   Horticulture

SOUTH YORKSHIRE
Barnsley College of Technology
Doncaster Metropolitan Insitute of
   Higher Education
Granville College of Further
   Education
Rockingham College of Further
   Education
Rother Valley College of Further
   Education

STAFFORDSHIRE
Staffordshire College of Agriculture
Staffordshire Technical College

SUFFOLK
Suffolk Farm Training Centre
Otley College of Agriculture &
   Horticulture

SURREY
Merrist Wood Agricultural College
North East Surrey College of
   Technology

TYNE & WEAR
Monkwearmouth College of Further
   Education

WARWICKSHIRE
South Warwickshire College of
  Further Education
Warwickshire College of Agriculture
See also West Midlands

WEST MIDLANDS
Bournville College of Further
  Education
College of Technology & Art
Hall Green Technical College
Matthew Boulton Technical College
Solihull College of Technology
Tile Hill College of Further
  Education
Wulfrun College of Further
  Education
See also Warwickshire

WEST SUSSEX
West Sussex College of Agriculture

WEST YORKSHIRE
Airdale and Wharfdale College of
  Further Education
Huddersfield Technical College
The Percival Whitley College of
  Further Education
Wakefield District College

WILTSHIRE
Lackham College of Agriculture

WORCESTERSHIRE
See Hereford & Worcester

Wales

CLWYD
Welsh College of Horticulture

DYFED
Ceredigion College of Further
  Education

GWENT
College of Agriculture

GWYNEDD
Coleg Pencraig
University College of North Wales

MID GLAMORGAN
Mid Glamorgan College of
  Agriculture & Horticulture

POWYS
Coleg Howell Harris

SOUTH GLAMORGAN
South Glamorgan Institute of Higher
  Education

WEST GLAMORGAN
Port Talbot College of Further
  Education
Swansea College

Northern Ireland

Belfast College of Technology
College of Further Education

Eire

National Botanic Gardens

Channel Islands

Guernsey College of Further Education
Highlands College

National Certificate Courses

Duration generally one year, full time.
Entrance requirements: Minimum age
17, candidates with GCSEs, City &
Guilds or NVQs may be given
preference.

NC IN HORTICULTURE

England

BERKSHIRE
Berkshire College of Agriculture

CAMBRIDGE
Cambridge College of Agriculture &
 Horticulture

CHESHIRE
Reaseheath College of Agriculture

CORNWALL
Duchy College of Agriculture &
 Horticulture

DERBYSHIRE
Broomfield College

DEVON
Bicton College of Agriculture

DORSET
Kingston Maurwood College

DURHAM
Houghall College

GLOUCESTERSHIRE
Hartpury College

HAMPSHIRE
Sparsholt College

HERTFORDSHIRE
Oaklands College

HUMBERSIDE
Bishop Burton College of
 Agriculture

KENT
Hadlow College of Agriculture &
 Horticulture

LANCASHIRE
Lancashire College of Agriculture &
 Horticulture

LEICESTERSHIRE
Brooksby College

LINCOLNSHIRE
Lincolnshire College of Agriculture &
 Horticulture

MIDDLESEX
Norwood Hall Centre for
 Environmental Services

NORFOLK
Norfolk College of Agriculture &
 Horticulture

NORTHAMPTONSHIRE
Moulton College

NOTTINGHAMSHIRE
Brackenhurst College

SOMERSET
Cannington College

STAFFORDSHIRE
Staffordshire College of Agriculture

SUFFOLK
Otley College of Agriculture &
 Horticulture

SURREY
Merrist Wood College

WARWICKSHIRE
Warwickshire College

WEST SUSSEX
Brinsby College

WILTSHIRE
Lackham College

WORCESTERSHIRE
Pershore College of Horticulture

YORKSHIRE
Askham Bryan College

Wales

Welsh College of Horticulture

Scotland

DUMFRIES & GALLOWAY
Threave School of Gardening

FIFE
Elmwood College

GRAMPIAN
Aberdeen College of Further
   Education

LOTHIAN
Oatridge Agricultural College

STRATHCLYDE
Langside College

TAYSIDE
Angus College of Further Education
Dundee College of Further Education

NORTHERN IRELAND

Greenmount College of Agriculture
   & Horticulture

National Certificate Courses in Related Subjects

NC IN AMENITY HORTICULTURE/ LANDSCAPE CONSTRUCTION
Oaklands College
Oatridge College (SCOTVEC course)

NC IN ARBORICULTURE
Aberdeen College (SCOTVEC course)
Cannington College
Lancashire College

NC IN COMMERCIAL HORTICULTURE
Brinsbury College
Oaklands College
Welsh College

NC IN GARDEN CENTRE OPERATION
Lancashire College

NC IN GOLF COURSE MANAGEMENT
Oatridge College (SCOTVEC
   course)

NC IN GREENKEEPING & SPORTSTURF MANAGEMENT
Oatridge College (SCOTVEC
   course)

NC IN GROUNDSMANSHIP & GREENKEEPING
Lancashire College

NC IN HORTICULTURAL ENGINEERING
Oatridge College (SCOTVEC
   course)

NC IN INTERIOR LANDSCAPING
Oaklands College

NC IN LANDSCAPE PRACTICE
Lancashire College

NC IN NURSERY PRACTICE
Lancashire College

Countryside and Leisure Management

NC IN COUNTRYSIDE & RELATED SKILLS
Broomfield College
Hartpury College
Otley College

NC IN LAND USE &
COUNTRYSIDE SKILLS
Walford College

NC IN PRACTICAL HABITAT
MANAGEMENT
Merrist Wood College

Forestry

NC IN FORESTRY
Inverness College

Advanced National Certificate Courses

Duration generally one year, full time
or 'thin' sandwich. Entrance
requirements: minimum age 18,
candidates should hold a NCH or
Phase II City and Guilds (replaced by
NVQ).

Horticulture and Related Subjects

ANC IN COMMERCIAL FRUIT
PRODUCTION & MARKETING
Hadlow College

ANC GREENKEEPING
Warwickshire College

ANC IN HORTICULTURE
Brooksby College
Cannington College
Hartpury College
Pershore College
Warwickshire College

HNC IN HORTICULTURE
(SCOTVEC)
Scottish Agricultural College

HNC LANDSCAPE
MANAGEMENT (SCOTVEC)
Oatridge College

HNC SPORTSTURF
MANAGEMENT (SCOTVEC)
Oatridge College

First Diploma Courses

Duration generally one year, full time.
A BTEC First National Diploma is a
vocational course which enables
students to progress onto a National
Diploma and therefore replaces the
four GCSE minimum entrance
requirement of many colleges.

Countryside and Leisure Management

1ST DIPLOMA IN
CONSERVATION & WILDLIFE
HABITAT MANAGEMENT
Hartpury College

1ST DIPLOMA IN LEISURE &
RECREATION
Walford College

1ST DIPLOMA IN OUTDOOR
RECREATION & LEISURE
Hartpury College

1ST DIPLOMA IN RURAL
BUSINESS ADMINISTRATION
Staffordshire College

1ST DIPLOMA IN RURAL
LEISURE
Hartpury College

1ST DIPLOMA IN RURAL
STUDIES
Stourbridge College

1ST DIPLOMA IN
RURAL/COUNTRYSIDE SKILLS
Bloomfield College
Cambridgeshire College
Cannington College
Capel Manor Centre
Staffordshire College

Forestry

1ST DIPLOMA IN FORESTRY
BUSINESS & FINANCE
Lincolnshire College

Horticulture and Related Subjects

1ST DIPLOMA IN
ARBORICULTURE
Holme Lacy College

1ST DIPLOMA IN COMMERCIAL
HORTICULTURE
Warwickshire College

1ST DIPLOMA IN GARDEN
CENTRE RETAILING
Berkshire College

1ST DIPLOMA IN GOLF STUDIES
Reaseheath College

1ST DIPLOMA IN
GREENKEEPING
Oaklands College

1ST DIPLOMA IN
HORTICULTURE
Askham Bryan College
Aylesbury College
Berkshire College
Bicton College
Bishop Burton College

Brinsbury College
Broomfield College
Cambridgeshire College
Cannington College
Capel Manor Centre
Hadlow College
Hall Green College
Hartpury College
Houghall College
Lincolnshire College
Moulton College
Norton Radstock College
Oaklands College
Pencoed College
Reaseheath College
South London College
Sparsholt College
Staffordshire College
Stoke-on-Trent College
Walford College
Writtle College

1ST DIPLOMA IN HORTICULTURE
& LANDSCAPING
Newton Rigg College

1ST DIPLOMA IN HORTICULTURAL
MECHANISATION
Cannington College
Oaklands College

National Diploma Courses

Duration: generally three years, sandwich courses. Entrance requirements: minimum age 18, candidates should hold 4 GCSEs or a First National Diploma. Twelve months pre-entry work in horticulture is normally required.

Business

ND IN BUSINESS STUDIES & FINANCE
Norfolk College
Oaklands College
Welsh College

Countryside and Leisure Management

ND IN CONSERVATION & WILDLIFE HABITAT MANAGEMENT
Hartpury College

ND IN COUNTRYSIDE MANAGEMENT
Cambridgeshire College
Cannington College
National Trust
Norfolk College

ND IN COUNTRYSIDE RECREATION
Merrist Wood College

ND IN ENVIRONMENTAL LANDSCAPE MANAGEMENT
Lincolnshire College

ND IN LAND USE & RECREATION
Houghall College
Walford College

ND IN LEISURE ATTRACTION MANAGEMENT
Lackham College

ND IN RURAL BUSINESS MANAGEMENT
Cannington College

ND IN RURAL STUDIES
Stourbridge College

ND IN TOURISM & COUNTRYSIDE MANAGEMENT
Lackham College

Horticulture and Related Subjects

ND IN AMENITY HORTICULTURE
Askham College
Cambridgeshire College
Cannington College
Elmwood College
Hartpury College
Kingston Maurwood College
National Trust
Writtle College

ND IN AMENITY/LANDSCAPE STUDIES
Brinsbury College
Hadlow College

ND IN ARBORICULTURE
Merrist Wood College

ND IN COMMERCIAL HORTICULTURE
Hadlow College
Oaklands College
Writtle College

ND IN ENGINEERING & EUROPEAN STUDIES
Cannington College

ND IN GARDEN CENTRE RETAILING
Hadlow College

ND IN HORTICULTURE
Berkshire College
Bicton College
Hadlow College
Houghall College
Lackham College
Lancashire College

Pencoed College
Pershore College
Scottish Agricultural College
Sparsholt College
Staffordshire College

ND IN HORTICULTURAL ENGINEERING & MECHANISATION
Askham Bryan College

ND IN LANDSCAPE & AMENITY HORTICULTURE
Reaseheath College

ND IN LANDSCAPE CONSTRUCTION
Merrist Wood College
Oatridge College

ND IN PLANT PRODUCTION & GARDEN CENTRE MANAGEMENT
Merrist Wood College

ND IN TURF SCIENCE & SPORTSGROUND MAINTENANCE
Lancashire College

ND IN URBAN FORESTRY
Askham Bryan College

Higher National Diploma Courses

Duration: generally three years, sandwich course. Entrance requirements: minimum age 18. Candidates should hold a BTEC National Diploma, NCH, Phase II City and Guilds or approved SCOTVEC qualification or hold 1 A Level (and have studied for another), 4 GCSEs, and have 12 months pre-entry horticultural work experience.

Countryside and Leisure Management

HND IN COUNTRYSIDE AND LEISURE RECREATION
Merrist Wood College

HND IN LEISURE MANAGEMENT
Scottish Agricultural College

HND IN RECREATIONAL LAND MANAGEMENT
Lancashire College

HND IN RURAL RESOURCE MANAGEMENT
Writtle College

Forestry

HND IN FORESTRY
Inverness College

Horticulture and Related Subjects

HND IN GOLF COURSE MANAGEMENT
Elmswood College (SCOTVEC course)
Merrist Wood College
Reaseheath College

HND IN GOLF GREENKEEPING WITH EUROPEAN STUDIES
Cannington College

HND IN HORTICULTURE
Askham College
University of Central England in Birmingham
in conjunction with Pershore College
University of Greenwich
in conjunction with Hadlow College
Hadlow College
in conjunction with University of Greenwich

Lincolnshire College
Pershore College
in conjunction with University of
    Central England in Birmingham
Scottish Agricultural College
Welsh College

HND IN HORTICULTURE WITH EUROPEAN STUDIES
Cannington College

HND IN LANDSCAPE & AMENITY MANAGEMENT
Writtle College

HND IN LANDSCAPE CONTRACT MANAGEMENT
Merrist Wood College

Degree Courses

First Degrees

Duration of courses varies: the number of years and the course structure (FT = full time courses/ SW = sandwich courses) of each degree is on the right. Entrance requirements. generally three 'A' Levels, although some universities accept National Diplomas in suitable subjects.

BSc (HONS) AGRICULTURAL AND ENVIRONMENTAL SCIENCE
University of Newcastle	3FT
Wye College	3FT

BSc (HONS) APPLIED BIOLOGY (AGRICULTURAL BIOLOGY)
University of Hertfordshire	4SW

BSc (HONS) APPLIED AND ENVIRONMENTAL BIOLOGY
University of York	3FT

BSc (HONS) APPLIED BIOLOGY AND CROP PROTECTION
University College (Wales)	3FT

BSc (HONS) APPLIED PLANT SCIENCE
University of Manchester	4SW
University of York	3FT

BSc ARBORICULTURE & ENVIRONMENTAL FORESTRY
University of Aberdeen	4FT

BSc (HONS) COMBINED STUDIES (ENVIRONMENTAL STUDIES OPTION)
Manchester Polytechnic	3FT/4SW/5PT

BSc (HONS) COUNTRYSIDE MANAGEMENT
University of Newcastle	3FT
Wye College	3FT

BSc CROP AND SOIL SCIENCE
University College (Wales)	3FT

BSc (HONS) CROP TECHNOLOGY AND RESOURCE MANAGEMENT
University of Bath	4SW

BSc (HONS) ECOLOGY
University of Lancaster	3FT
University of Sterling	4FT
University of York	3FT

BSc ECOLOGICAL STUDIES
University of Edinburgh	4FT

BSc (HONS) ENVIRONMENTAL BIOLOGY
Royal Holloway and New Bedford College	3FT

BSc (HONS) ENVIRONMENTAL MANAGEMENT
Manchester Polytechnic	3FT/4SW/5PT

BSc ENVIRONMENTAL SCIENCE
University of Aberdeen	3FT

Manchester Polytechnic 3FT/4SW/5PT
University of Sterling 4FT
Wye College 3FT

BSc ENVIRONMENT STUDIES
Crewe and Alsager College 3FT
University of Hertfordshire 4SW
University of Newcastle 3FT
Wye College (Hons) 3FT

BSc ESTATE MANAGEMENT
University of Northumbria at
Newcastle 3FT
University of Greenwich 3FT/4SW/5PT

BSc FORESTRY
University of Aberdeen (Hons) 4FT
University of Edinburgh 4FT
University College (Wales) 3FT

BSc HORTICULTURE
University of Hertfordshire 4SW
University of Nottingham 3FT
University of Reading 3FT/4SW
University of Strathclyde 3FT/4SW
Wye College 3FT/4SW

BSc (HONS) HORTICULTURE
Hadlow College with University of
Greenwich 4SW
University of Hertfordshire 4SW
University of Nottingham 3FT
University of Reading 3FT/4SW
University of Strathclyde 3FT/4SW
Writtle College with University of
Hertfordshire 4SW
Wye College 3FT/4SW

BSc HORTICULTURAL BUSINESS MANAGEMENT
Wye College 3FT

BSc HORTICULTURE WITH EUROPEAN STUDIES
University of Nottingham 4FT

BSc HORTICULTURE WITH HORTICULTURAL MANAGEMENT
University of Strathclyde 3FT/4SW

BSc (HONS) HORTICULTURAL TECHNOLOGY AND MANAGEMENT
Lancashire College 4FT

BA (HONS) LANDSCAPE AND ARCHAEOLOGY
University of Sheffield 3FT

BSc (HONS) LANDSCAPE MANAGEMENT
University of Reading 4SW

BSc (HONS) LANDSCAPE DESIGN AND PLANT SCIENCE
University of Sheffield 3FT

BSc (HONS) LANDSCAPE MANAGEMENT
University of Reading 4SW

BSc LANDSCAPE STUDIES WITH PLANT SCIENCE
Sheffield University 3FT

BSc (HONS) PLANT BIOCHEMISTRY
Royal Holloway and New Bedford
College 3FT

BSc PLANT BIOLOGY
Royal Holloway and New Bedford
College (Hons) 3FT
University of Manchester 3FT

BSc RURAL ENVIRONMENTAL STUDIES
University of Aberdeen (Hons) 4FT
University of Edinburgh (Hons) 4FT
University College (Wales) (Hons) 3FT
Wye College 3FT

BSc RURAL RESOURCE
MANAGEMENT
Silsoe College (Hons)   4SW
University College (Wales)   3FT

Post Graduate Studies

Duration: generally 1 year, full time.

GCERT LANDSCAPE STUDIES
University of Sheffield

GD LANDSCAPE
ARCHITECTURE
Leeds Metropolitan University
University of Sheffield
University of Greenwich

M ARCH STUDIES IN
LANDSCAPE
University of Sheffield

MA LANDSCAPE DESIGN
University of Sheffield

MA LANDSCAPE MANAGEMENT
Manchester University

MSc AGRICULTURE AND
AMENITY GRASSLAND
Aberystwyth University

MSc AGRICULTURAL BOTANY
Aberystwyth University

MSc AGRICULTURAL
ENGINEERING
Silsoe College

MSc APPLIED ENTOMOLOGY
AND CROP PROTECTION
University of Newcastle

MSc APPLIED PLANT SCIENCE
Wye College

MSc CONSERVATION
University College (London)

MSc CONSERVATION AND SOIL
FERTILITY
Wye College

MSc COUNTRYSIDE
MANAGEMENT
Manchester Polytechnic

MSc ECOLOGY
University of Aberdeen
Crewe and Alsager College

MSc ENVIRONMENTAL
RESOURCES
University of Salford

MSc ENVIRONMENTAL SCIENCE
University of Aberdeen

MSc FORESTRY
University of Aberdeen
Bangor, University of Wales

MSc FRUIT PRODUCTION
Wye College

MSc/DIP HORTICULTURE
University of Reading

MSc INTEGRATED PEST &
DISEASE MANAGEMENT
Wye College

MSc LANDSCAPE ECOLOGY,
DESIGN & MANAGEMENT
Wye College

MSc PLANT BIOTECHNOLOGY
Wye College

MSc TROPICAL & SUB-TROPICAL
HORTICULTURAL & CROP
SCIENCE
Wye College

Addresses

Note: * indicates those colleges also running a wide range of part-time courses on a day release, block release or evening basis – including City and Guilds, NVQs, SCOTVECs and other courses in horticulture, floristry and related subjects.

Aberdeen College of Further Education*
School of Rural Studies, Clinterty, Kinellar, Aberdeen, Grampian AB2 0TN

Aberdeen, University of
Department of Agriculture, 581 King Street, Aberdeen, Grampian AB9 1UD

Aberdeen, University of
Department of Forestry, St Machar Drive, Aberdeen, Grampian AB9 2UD

Aberystwyth University
(University College of Wales), Department of Agricultural Sciences, Penlais, Aberystwyth, Dyfed SY23 3DD

ACOT National Office
Frascati Road, Blackrock, County Dublin, Eire

Amenity Horticulture, College of *
National Botanic Gardens, Glasnevin, Dublin 9, Eire

An Grianan, College of, Horticulture
Termonfeckin, County Louth, Eire

Angus College of Further Education *
Keptie Road, Arbroath, Tayside DD11 3EA

Askham Bryan College *
Askham Bryan, York YO2 3PR

Aylesbury College *
Hampden Hall, Wendover Road, Stoke Mandeville, Buckinghamshire HP22 5TB

Bangor (University of Wales)
School of Agricultural & Forest Sciences, University College of North Wales, Deiniol Road, Bangor, Gwynedd LL57 2UW

Berkshire College of Agriculture *
Hall Place, Burchetts Green, Maidenhead, Berkshire SL6 6QR

Bicton College of Agriculture*
East Buddleigh, Devon EX9 7BY

Bishop Burton College of Agriculture *
Bishop Burton, Beverley, North Humberside HU17 8QG

Blaise Training Centre *
Kingsweston Road, Lawrence Weston, Bristol, Avon BS11 0XF

Brackenhurst College
Brackenhurst, Southwell, Nottinghamshire NG25 0QF

Brighton College of Technology *
Pelham Street, Brighton, Sussex BN1 4FA

Brinsby College *
(West Sussex College of Agriculture & Horticulture), North Heath, Pulborough, West Sussex RH20 1DL

Brooksby College *
Brooksby, Melton Mowbray, Leicestershire LE14 2LJ

Broomfield College *
Morley, Derby DE7 6DN

Cambridgeshire College of Agriculture & Horticulture *
Cambridge Centre: (Also

Cambridgeshire Farm College),
Landbeach Road, Milton, Cambridge
CB4 4DB

Sawtry Centre:
Green End Road, Sawtry,
Huntingdon, Cambridgeshire
PE17 5UY

Wisbech Centre:
Newcommon Bridge, Wisbech,
Cambridgeshire PE13 2SJ

Cannington College *
Cannington, Bridgwater, Somerset
TA5 2LS

**Capel Manor Horticultural &
Environmental Centre** *
Bullsmoor Lane, Enfield, Middlesex
EN1 4RQ

**Central England in Birmingham,
University of**
School of Landscape, Faculty of the
Built Environment, Birmingham
Polytechnic, Perry Bar, Birmingham,
West Midlands B42 2SU

**Cheltenham & Gloucester College of
Higher Education**
Department of Countryside &
Landscape, Francis Close, Hall
Campus, Swindon Road, Cheltenham,
Gloucestershire GL50 4AZ

Cheshire College of Agriculture
Reaseheath, Nantwich, Cheshire
CW5 6DF

Cranfield Institute of Technology
Silsoe College, Silsoe, Bedfordshire
MK45 4DT

Dorset College of Agriculture
(see Kingston Maurward College)

Dublin, University College
Department of Horticulture, Belfield,
Dublin, Eire

**Duchy College of Agriculture &
Horticulture** *
West Cornwall Centre, Pool, Redruth,
Cornwall TR15 3RD

Dundee College of Further Education *
Old Glamis Road, Dundee, Tayside
DD3 8LE

**Durham College of Agriculture and
Horticulture**
(see Houghall College)

Edinburgh, University of
Department of Forestry & Natural
Resources, Darwin Building, King's
Building, Mayfield Road, Edinburgh
EH9 3JU

Edinburgh, University of
Department of Landscape
Architecture, 20 Chambers Street,
Edinburgh EH1 1JZ

Elmwood College *
Cupar, Fife KY15 4JB

Evesham College of Further Education
Cheltenham Road, Evesham,
Worcestershire WR11 4LX

Farnborough College of Technology
Boundary Road, Farnborough,
Hampshire GU14 6SB

Finchale Training College *
Durham DH1 5RX

Garden Design, College of
Admin Office:
Cothelstone, Taunton, Somerset
TA4 3DP

Greenmount College of Agriculture & Horticulture
Antrim, County Antrim, Northern Ireland BT41 4PU

Greenwich, University of
Dartford Campus, Oakfield Lane, Dartford, Kent DA1 2SZ

Guisborough Agricultural Centre
Avenue Place, off Redcar Road, Guisborough, Cleveland TS14 6AX

Hadlow College of Agriculture & Horticulture *
Hadlow, Tonbridge, Kent TN11 0AL

Hall Green College *
Cole Bank Road, Birmingham B28 8ES

Hampstead Garden Suburb Adult Education Centre
The Institute, Central Square, London NW11 7BN

Hartpury College *
Hartpury House, Hartpury, Gloucestershire GL19 3BE

Hereford College of Agriculture
(see Holme Lacey College)

Heriot Watt University/Edinburgh College of Art
Department of Landscape Architecture, Lauriston Place, Edinburgh EH3 9DF

Hertfordshire College of Agriculture and Horticulture
(see Oaklands College)

Hertfordshire, University of
School of Natural Sciences, College Lane, Hatfield, Hertfordshire AL10 9AB

Holme Lacey College *
Holme Lacey, Hereford HR2 6LL

Horticultural Correspondence College
Little Notton Farmhouse, 16 Notton, Lacock, Chippenham, Wiltshire SN15 2NF

Horticultural Therapy
Goulds Ground, Valis Way, Frome, Somerset BA11 3DW

Houghall College *
(Durham College of Agriculture & Horticulture), Houghall, Durham DH1 3SG

Huddersfield Technical College *
New North Road, Huddersfield, West Yorkshire HD1 5NN

International Correspondence Schools
312–14 High Street, Sutton, Surrey SM1 1PR
also
36 Hillcourt Road, Glenageary, Dun Loaghaire, County Dublin, Eire
also:
Intertext House, 8 Elliot Place, Clydeway Centre, Glasgow G3 8EF

Inverness College *
3 Longman Road, Longman South, Inverness IV1 1SA

Isle of Wight College of Arts & Technology *
Medina Way, Newport, Isle of Wight PO30 5TA

Kildalton Agricultural & Horticultural College
Piltown, County Kilkenny, Eire

Kingston Maurward *
(The Dorset College of Agriculture & Horticulture), Dorchester, Dorset DT2 8PY

Kirkley Hall College *
Kirkley Hall, Ponteland, Newcastle-upon-Tyne NE20 0AQ

Knowsley Community College *
Horticulture Centre, Knowsley Park,
Prescot, Merseyside L34 4AQ

Lackham College *
Lacock, Chippenham, Wiltshire
SN15 2NY

**Lancashire College of Agriculture &
Horticulture** *
Myerscought Hall, Bilsborrow,
Preston, Lancashire PR3 0RY

Langside College *
50 Prospecthill Road, Glasgow
G42 9LB

Leeds Metropolitan University
Calverley Street, Leeds LS1 3HE
also:
Department of Architecture &
Landscape

**Lincolnshire College of Agriculture &
Horticulture** *
Caythorpe Court, Caythorpe,
Grantham, Lincolnshire NG32 3EP
also:
Riseholme Hall, Riseholme, Lincoln
LN2 2LG

Loughborough College
Radmoor, Loughborough,
Leicestershire LE11 3BT

Manchester Metropolitan University
Department of Environmental &
Geographical Studies, Faculty of
Community Studies, John Dalton
Building, Chester Street, Manchester
M1 5GD

Manchester, University of
School of Landscape, Department of
Planning & Landscape, Oxford Road,
Manchester M13 9PL

Merrist Wood College *
Worplesdon, Guildford, Surrey
GU3 3PE

**Mid-Kent College of Higher & Further
Education** *
Oakwood Park, Tonbridge Road,
Maidstone, Kent ME16 8AQ

Moulton College *
Moulton, Northampton NN3 1RR

Newcastle, University of
Faculty of Agriculture (and
Department of Town Country
Planning), Claremount Tower,
Newcastle-upon-Tyne NE1 7R

Newton Rigg College *
Penrith, Cumbria CA11 0AH

Newton Training
The Old Estate Yard, Newton St Loe,
Bath, Avon BA2 9BR

**Norfolk College of Agriculture &
Horticulture** *
Easton, Norwich, Norfolk NR9 5DX

**North East Surrey College of
Technology** *
Reigate Road, Ewell, Epsom, Surrey
KT17 3DS

**Northamptonshire College of
Agriculture and Horticulture**
(see Moulton College)

Northumbria College of Agriculture
(see Kirkley College)

**Northumbria at Newcastle, Univeristy
of**
Ellison Building, Ellison Place,
Newcastle-upon-Tyne NE1 8ST

**Norton Radstock College of Further
Education** *
South Hill Park, Radstock, Bath, Avon
BA3 3RW

Norwood Hall Centre for Environmental Services *
(Ealing Tertiary College), Norwood Green, Southall, Middlesex UB2 4LA

Nottingham, University of
School of Agriculture, Sutton Bonnington, Loughborough, Leicester LE12 5RD

Nottinghamshire College of Agriculture
(see Brackenhurst College)

Oaklands College *
St Albans, Hertfordshire AL4 0JA

Oatridge Agricultural College *
Ecclesmachan, Broxburn, West Lothian EH52 6NH

Otley College of Agriculture & Horticulture *
Otley, Ipswich, Suffolk IP6 9EY

The Oundle Area Adult Education Centre
Prince William School, Herne Road, Oundle, Peterborough, Cambridgeshire PE6 4BS

Pencoed College *
Pencoed, Bridgend, Mid Glamorgan CF35 5LG

Pershore College of Horticulture *
Pershore, Worcestershire WR10 3JP

Perth College of Further Education *
Crieff Road, Perth, Tayside PH1 2NX

Plumpton Agricultural College *
Lewes, East Sussex BN7 3AE

Reading, University of
Department of Horticulture, School of Plant Sciences, University of Reading, Whiteknights, PO Box 221, Reading, Berkshire RG6 2AS

Reaseheath College *
(Cheshire College of Agriculture), Reaseheath, Nantwich, Cheshire CW5 6DF

Royal Botanic Garden
20A Inverleith Row, Edinburgh EH3 5LR

Royal Botanic Gardens
School of Horticulture, Kew, Richmond, Surrey TW9 3AB

Royal Holloway & New Bedford College*
(University of London), Department of Biology, Egham Hill, Egham, Surrey TW20 0EX

St Helens Community College *
Newton Campus, Crow Lane East, Newton-le-Willows, Merseyside WA12 9TT

Salesian College of Horticulture
Warrenstown, Drumree, County Neath, Eire

Scottish Agricultural College *
Auchincruive, Ayr, Strathclyde KA6 5HW

Sheffield, University of
Department of Landscape, University of Sheffield, Sheffield, South Yorkshire S10 2TN

Shipley College
Exhibition Road, Shipley, West Yorkshire BD18 3JW

Shropshire College of Further Education
Stourbridge Road, Bridgnorth, Salop WV15 6AL

Silsoe College
(see Cranfield Institute of Technology)

Solihull College of Technology *
Blossomfield Road, Solihull, West
Midlands B91 1SB

South London College *
Knights Hill, West Norwood, London
SE27 0TX

South Manchester College *
(Wythenshawe Park Centre), Moor
Road, Manchester M23 9BQ

**South Warwickshire College of Further
Education** *
The Willows, Alcester Road, Stratford-
on-Avon, Warwickshire CV37 6NZ

Sparsholt College *
Sparsholt, Winchester, Hampshire
SO21 2NF

Stockton/Billingham Technical College
Causeway, Billingham, Cleveland
TS23 2DB

Staffordshire College of Agriculture *
Rodbaston, Penkridge, Stafford
ST19 5PH

Stoke-on-Trent College *
Burslem Campus, Moorland Road,
Burslem, Stoke-on-Trent, Staffordshire
ST6 1JJ

**Stourbridge College of Technology &
Art** *
Stourbridge College Horticultural
Unit, Leasowes Park Nursery,
Leasowes Lane, Halesowen, West
Midlands B62 8QF

Strathclyde, University of
McCance Building, 16 Richmond
Street, Glasgow G1 1XG

Tameside College of Technology
Beaufort Road, Ashton-under-Lyme,
Tameside, Greater Manchester
OL6 6NX

Threave School of Gardening
Castle Douglas, Dumfries and
Galloway DG7 1RX

Walford College of Agriculture *
Horticultural Education, Radbrook
Centre, Radbrook Road, Shrewsbury,
Shropshire SY3 9BL

Warwickshire College *
Moreton Morrell, Warwick CV35 9BL

Welsh College of Horticulture *
Northop, Mold, Clwyd CH7 6AA

Wigan College of Technology
Parsons Walk, Wigan, Lancashire
WN1 1RR

Worcestershire College of Agriculture *
Hindlip, Worcester WR3 8SS

Writtle College *
Chelmsford, Essex CM1 3RR

Wulfrun College *
Department of Applied Science, Paget
Road, Wolverhampton, West Midlands
WV6 0DU

Wye College
(University of London), Ashford, Kent
TN25 5AH

Gardening for the Disabled and Elderly

Though there is always room for improvement, the needs of elderly and disabled gardeners have been realistically addressed over the past decade or so. Consequently there is much available in the way of special tools and equipment and many gardens open to the public cater for special needs.

There are also, of course, many specialist organizations which cater for particular areas of disabled gardening. If you are disabled yourself or care for a disabled person, they'll be able to help with guidance on how to get the best out of your gardening.

National Trust Gardens Accessible to the Disabled

Key: W – wheelchairs provided

    * – Beware!

    GF – access to ground floor of house only

SHS – special hearing scheme – guides have been trained to understand special requirements of hearing impaired people

ENGLAND

AVON
Dyrham Park, Nr Chippenham   W   Taped guide

BERKSHIRE
Basildon Park, Lower Basildon,   W
   Reading

BUCKINGHAMSHIRE

Claydon House, Nr Buckingham	W	Guided tours GF
Cliveden, Maidenhead	W	Scented rose garden
Hughenden Manor, High Wycombe	W	Braille and taped guides Avoid Sundays and bank holidays
Stowe Landscape Gardens, Buckingham		Battery-powered self drive cars

CAMBRIDGESHIRE

Anglesey Abbey, Lode, Cambridge	W	Scented plants, Hyacinth garden, Braille guide Busy weekends, bank holidays and August
Wimpole Hall, Arrington, Royston	W	Braille guide

CHESHIRE

Dunham Massey Hall, Altrincham	W	* Cobbled area, * Canal trips SHS
Little Moreton Hall, Congleton	W	SHS GF
Tatton Park, Knutsford	W	

CORNWALL

Cotehele House, St Dominick, Saltash	W	Roses and other scented plants Busy afternoons
Lanhydrock, Bodmin	W	Busy Sundays, bank holidays, school holidays
Trelissick Garden, Nr Truro	W	Aromatic garden
Trengwainton Garden, Nr Penzance	W	Rhododendrons, streams
Trerice, Nr Newquay	W	

CUMBRIA		
Acorn Bank Garden, Temple Sowerby, Penrith		Herb garden, beck
Sizergh Castle Garden, Nr Kendal	W	Rock garden
DERBYSHIRE		
Calke Abbey, Ticknall	W	
Hardwick Hall, Doe Lea, Chesterfield		Walled flower garden, orchard, herb garden Busy at weekends, bank holidays and August
Kedleston Hall, Derby	W	Make prior arrangements before visit
DEVON		
Arlington Court, Nr Barnstaple	W	Make prior arrangements before visit
Buckland Abbey, Yelverston	W	Braille guide,* herb garden on steep slope
Castle Drogo, Drewsteignton	W	Scented plants
Killerton House & Garden, Exeter	W	Motorized buggy
Knightshayes Court & Garden, Tiverton	W	
Saltram House, Plympton	W	
GLOUCESTERSHIRE		
Hidcote Manor Garden, Chipping Campden	W	
Westbury Court Garden, Westbury on Severn	W	
HAMPSHIRE		
Hinton Ampner, Alresford	W	
Mottisfont Abbey Garden, Nr Romsey	W	Rose garden
The Vyne, Sherborne St John, Basingstoke	W	Make prior arrangements before visit

HEREFORD & WORCESTER

Berrington Hall, Leominster	W	
Croft Castle, Leominster	W	
Hanbury Hall, Droitwich	W	Braille guide

HERTFORDSHIRE

Shaw's Corner, Ayot St Lawrence, Welwyn	W	Make prior arrangements before visit

KENT

Chartwell, Westerham	W	
Emmetts Garden, Ide Hill, Sevenoaks	W	Motorized buggy, fountain and waterfall
Ightham Mote, Ivy Hatch, Sevenoaks	W	
Scotney Castle Garden, Lamberhurst	W	
Sissington Castle Garden, Nr Cranbrook	W	Special plan

LANCASHIRE

Gawthorpe Hall, Padiham	W	Make prior arrangements before visit
Rufford Old Hall, Ormskirk	W	

LINCOLNSHIRE

Belton House, Grantham	W	
Gunby Hall, Spilsby	W	Rose and herb garden

LONDON

Ham House, Richmond	W	Make prior arrangements before visit

MERSEYSIDE

Speke Hall, Liverpool	W	GF SHS

NORFOLK		
Blickling Hall, Aylesham	W	Plant centre
		Braille guide
Felbrigg Hall, Norwich	W	GF
		Braille guide
Oxburgh Hall, King's Lynn	W	GF
NORTHAMPTONSHIRE		
Canons Ashby House, Daventry	W	Taped guide
NORTHUMBERLAND		
Wallington, Cambo, Morpeth	W	Powered scooter
		GF
		Make prior arrangements before visit
SHROPSHIRE		
Attingham Park, Shrewsbury	W	Braille guide
		SHS
Dudmaston, Quatt, Bridgnorth	W	GF
		SHS
SOMERSET		
Montacute House & Garden, Nr Yeovil	W	Braille guide
SUFFOLK		
Ickworth, Bury St Edmunds	W	Braille guide
Melford Hall, Sudbury	W	
SURREY		
Clandon Park, Nr Guildford	W	
Claremont Landscape Garden, Esher	W	
Hatchlands Park, Nr Guildford	W	
Polesden Lacy, Nr Dorking	W	Rose and lavender gardens
Winkworth Arboretum, Nr Godalming		

EAST SUSSEX		
Sheffield Park Garden, Uckfield	W	Bluebells and water
WEST SUSSEX		
Nymans Garden, Handcross, Nr Haywards Heath	W	Old roses, scented plants
Petworth House & Pleasure Grounds, Nr Midhurst	W	Make prior arrangements before visit
Standen, East Grinstead	W	GF
Wakehurst Place Garden, Ardingly, Haywards Heath	W	
TYNE & WEAR		
Washington Old Hall, Washington		Scented plants
WARWICKSHIRE		
Baddesley Clinton, Knowle, Solihull	W	
Charlecote Park, Wellsbourne, Stratford-upon-Avon	W	Braille guide SHS Video
Coughton Court, Alcester	W	GF
Packwood House, Lapworth, Solihull	W	
Upton House, Nr Banbury	W	GF Buggy available
WILTSHIRE		
Stourhead, Stourton, Warminster	W	Spread Eagle Inn, rhododendrons and azaleas
NORTH YORKSHIRE		
Beningborough Hall, Shipton-by-Beningborough	W	
Fountains Abbey, Ripon	W	Powered buggies

Minnington Hall, York		River, peacocks GF

WEST YORKSHIRE

East Riddlesdon Hall, Keighley		Braille guide, ⬚SHS

WALES

CLWYD

Erddig, Nr Wrexham	W	Make prior arrangements before visit GF Braille guide

GWYNEDD

Penrhyn Castle, Nr Bangor	W	Golf buggy GF Braille guide
Plas Newydd, Llanfairpwll, Anglesey	W	Braille guide

POWYS

Powis Castle		Scented plants Braille guide

NORTHERN IRELAND

ARMAGH

Ardress House, Portadown		GF ⬚SHS
The Argory		⬚SHS

DOWN

Castle Ward, Strangford, Downpatrick	W	Woodland and lake walks GF Cassette guides ⬚SHS
Mount Stewart, Newtownards	W	Lake, scented plants GF ⬚SHS

Rowallane, Saintfield, Ballynahanch	W	Scented plants Make prior arrangements before visit Special tours SHS
FERMANAGII Florence Court, Enniskillen	W	GF SHS
LONDONDERRY Springhill, Moneymore, Magherafelt		Herb garden SHS

SCOTLAND

HIGHLAND REGION Brodie Castle, Nr Forres, Moray	W	GF Audio guide
Inverewe Garden, Poolewe, Wester Ross	W	Special map Access to greenhouse
WEST REGION Brodick Castle, Isle of Arran	W	
Culzean Castle, Nr Maybole, Ayreshire	W	
Greenbank Garden, Clarkston, Glasgow	W	Raised beds Access to greenhouse
Threave Garden, Castle Douglas, Stewarty	W	
GRAMPIAN REGION Crathes Castle, Nr Banchory	W	

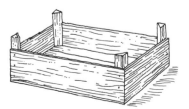

Suppliers of Tools for Easier Gardening

Better Methods-Europe
Brantwood House, Kimberley Road,
Parkstone, Poole, Dorset BH14 8SQ
Tel: (0202) 740142. Some mail order

Black and Decker
Westpoint, The Grove, Slough,
Berkshire SL1 1QQ
Tel: (0753) 79311

Blackwell Products
Unit 4, Riverside Industrial Estate,
Riverway, London SE10 0BH
Tel: (081) 305 1431. Mail order

Bob Andrews Ltd
Unit 1, Bilton Industrial Estate,
Lovelace Road, Bracknell, Berkshire
RG12 4YT
Tel: (0344) 862111

Bosmere Products Ltd
Northumberland Works,
Northumberland Road, Portsmouth,
Hampshire PO5 1DP
Tel: (0705) 863541. Mail order

Bridgedale (Felco)
Burton McCall Ltd, Samuel Street,
Leicester LE1 1RU
Tel: (0533) 538781. Mail order

CeKa Works Ltd
Pwllheli, Gwynedd LL53 5LH
Tel: (0758) 701070

Chase Organics (GB) Ltd
Coombe Lands, Addlestone,
Weybridge, Surrey KT15 1HY
Tel: (0932) 858511. Mail order

Cookson Plantpak
Mundon, Maldon, Essex CM9 8NT
Tel: (0621) 740140

JB Corrie and Co Ltd
Frenchmans Road, Petersfield,
Hampshire GU32 3AP
Tel: (0730) 62552/6

Croydex
North Way, Walworth Industrial
Estate, Andover, Hampshire
SP10 5AW
Tel: (0264) 65881

Dixon Farming and Garden Aids
168 Springdale Road, Corfe Mullen,
Wimbourne, Dorset BH21 3QN
Tel: (0202) 692194. Mail order

Easyreach
1 Innisfree Close, Harrogate, North
Yorkshire HG2 8PL
Tel: (0423) 883811. Mail order

Fiskars Ltd (Wilkinson Sword)
Brocastle Avenue, Waterton Industrial
Estate, Bridgend, South Glamorgan
CF31 3YN
Tel: (0656) 655595

Forest Fencing Ltd
Stanford Ct, Stanford Bridge,
Worcester WR6 6SR
Tel: (08865) 451. Mail order

Frank Odell Ltd
70 High Street, Teddington, Middlesex
TW11 8JE
Tel: (081) 8158/1007. Mail order

Flymo Ltd
Aycliffe Industrial Estate, Newtown,
Aycliffe, Co Durham DL5 6HD
Tel: (0325) 300303

Gardena (Distributed by Markt (UK) Ltd)
7 Dunhams Ct, Dunhams Lane,
Letchworth, Hertfordshire CM23 4BU
Tel: (0462) 686688

Geebo
Hailsham, East Sussex BN27 3DT
Tel: (0323) 840771

Geeco Ltd
Gore Road Industrial Estate, New
Milton, Hampshire BH25 6SE
Tel: (0425) 614600

Glenside Organics Ltd
Glenside Farm, Plean, Stirlingshire
FK7 8BA
Tel: (0876) 816655. Mail order

TH Grace Esq
Redford House, Wiggonholt,
Pulborough, West Sussex RH20 2EP
Tel: (0903) 742945. Mail order

Griffin Tools
Level Street, Brierley Hill, West
Midlands DY5 1UA
Tel: (0384) 77789

Hallgate Selection
Ash Priors, Taunton, Somerset
TA4 3NF
Tel: (0823) 257939. Mail order

Haws Elliot Ltd
Rawlings Road, Smethwick, Warley,
West Midlands B67 5AB
Tel: (021) 420 2494. Mail order

Helping Hand Co Ledbury Ltd
Unit L9, Bromyard Road Trading
Estate, Ledbury, Herefordshire
HR8 1NS
Tel: (0531) 5678. Mail order

Hills Industries Ltd
Pontygwindy Industrial Estate,
Caerphilly, Mid Glamorgan CF8 3HO
Tel: (0222) 883951

Homecraft Supplies Ltd
Low Moor Estate, Kirkby-in-Ashfield,
Nottinghamshire NG17 7JZ
Tel: (0623) 754047. Mail order

Howells of Sheffield
PO Box 383, Sheffield, Yorkshire
S8 0AT
Tel: (0742) 551072

Hozelock Ltd
Haddenham, Aylesbury,
Buckinghamshire HP17 8JD
Tel: (0844) 291881

ICI Garden Products
Woolmead House, East Woolmead
Walk, Farnham, Surrey GU9 7UB
Tel: (0252) 733919

Jenks and Cattell Ltd
Neachells Lane, Wednesfield,
Wolverhampton, West Midlands
WV11 3PU
Tel: (0902) 731271

Langdon (London) Ltd
5 Worminghall Road, Ickford,
Buckinghamshire HP18 9JJ
Tel: (08447) 337. Mail order

Michael Banks Marketing
Ruxley Ridge, Claygate, Esher, Surrey
KT10 0JE
Tel: (0372) 67922/3. Mail order

Metpost Ltd
Mardy Road, Cardiff CF3 8EQ
Tel: (0222) 777877

Multi-Purpose Garden Tools
Unit 1X, Dolphin Square, Bovey
Traccy, Devon TQ1 3AS
Tel: (0626) 833213

Organiser Belt Co
90 Orbel Street, London SW11 3NY
Tel: (081) 228 0668

QV Garden Products
Maidstone Road, Nettlestead,
Maidstone, Kent ME18 5HP
Tel: (0622) 871666. Mail order

Qualcast (Home and Garden Equipment) Ltd
Coleridge Street, Sunnyhill, Derby
DE3 7JT
Tel: (0332) 760202

Rainbow Tools (Sheffield) Ltd
Meadow Way, Swinton Meadows
Industrial Estate, Swinton,
Rotherham, South Yorkshire S64 8AB
Tel: (0709) 585817

Redashe
Unit 11, Hewitts Industrial Estate,
Elmbridge Road, Cranleigh, Surrey
GU6 8CW
Tel: (0483) 275774

RY, Robinson Young Ltd
Ibson House, Eastern Way, Bury St
Edmunds, Suffolk IP32 7AB
Tel: (0284) 766261

Rolcut Ltd
Blatchford Road, Horsham, West
Sussex RH13 5QU
Tel: (0403) 65997

Sow Easy Sales & Marketing Ltd
Celandine House, Templewood Lane,
Farnham Common, Buckinghamshire
SL2 3HF
Tel (0753) 644588

Spear and Jackson
Handsworth Road, Sheffield, South
Yorkshire S13 9BR
Tel: (0742) 449911

Standard Manufacturing Co
55 Woods Lane, Derby DE3 8UD
Tel: (0332) 43369

Tandown Products
Victoria House, Victoria Street,
Millbrook, Stalybridge, Tameside
SK15 3HX
Tel: (061) 303 1883. Mail order

Tollgate Tool Sales
Tollgate House, Tollgate Lane, Bury
St Edmunds, Suffolk IP32 6DG
Tel: (0284) 763636. Mail order

Tool-Mate Ltd
PO Box 58, Ipswich, Suffolk IP9 1PD
Tel: (047334) 749. Mail order

The Trailerbarrow Co
Elson House, Buxted, Sussex
TN22 4LW
Tel: (0825) 813291

A E Vince Patents
6 Penaber, Criccieth, Gwynedd
LL52 OES
Tel: (0766) 522454. Mail order

Weeder Ltd
Brick Heath Road, Wolverhampton,
West Midlands WV1 2ST
Tel: (0902) 352982

Wilkinson Sword
– *see* Fiskars

Wolf Tools Ltd
Alton Road, Ross-on-Wye,
Herefordshire HR9 5NE
Tel: (0989) 767600. Mail order

A Wright & Son Ltd
Midland Works, 16–18 Sidney Street,
Sheffield, South Yorkshire S1 4RH
Tel: (0742) 722677. Mail order

Resources for the Disabled

Advisory Committee For Blind Gardeners
c/o Mr Reg Cove, 55 Eton Avenue,
London NW3 3ET
Tel: 071 722 9703

The Arthritis and Rheumatism Council for Research
41 Eagle Street, London WC1R 4AR
Tel: 071 405 8572

Buckinghamshire Association for Gardening with Disabled People
c/o Bob Millard, 47 Station Road,
Winslow, Buckinghamshire MK18 3DZ
Tel: Winslow 2621

Cassette Library for Blind Gardeners
c/o Miss Kathleen Fleet, 48 Tolcarne
Drive, Pinner, Middlesex HA5 2DQ
Tel: 081 868 4026

The County Landowners Association (CLA)
Publishes *A Guide to Countryside Recreation for Disabled People*
CLA Publications Dept, 16 Belgrave
Square, London SW1X 8PQ
Tel: 081 235 0511

Disabled Living Foundation
380–4 Harrow Road, London W9 2HU
Tel: 071 289 6111

Federation to Promote Horticulture for the Disabled
The Drove, Gillingham, Dorset
SP8 4RE
Tel: 074 76 2369

The Garden Club
Church Cottage, Headcorn, Kent
TN27 9NP
Tel: 0622 890467

Gardens for the Disabled Trust
Hayes Farm House, Hayes Lane,
Peasmarsh, East Sussex TN31 6XR
Tel: 0622 890467

Herefordshire Growing Point
c/o Holme Lacy College of Agriculture
& Horticulture, Holme Lacy, Hereford
HR2 6LL
Tel: 043273 316

Horticultural Therapy
Goulds Ground, Vallias Wat. Frome,
Somerset BA11 3DW
Tel: 0373 464782

Joint Disabled Living Centres Council
c/o TRAIDS, 76 Clarendon Park
Road, Leicester LE2 3AD
Tel: 0533 700747/8

Mary Marlborough Lodge
Nuffield Orthopaedic Centre NHS
Trust, Windmill Road, Headington,
Oxford OX3 7LD
Tel: 0865 227593

MENCAP
123 Golden Lane, London EC1Y 0RT
Tel: 081 253 9433

National Library for the Blind
48 Tolcarne Drive, Pinner, Middlesex
HA5 2DQ
Tel: 081 868 4026

National Trust Gardens for the Disabled
The National Trust, 36 Queen Anne's
Gate, London SW1H 9AS
Tel: 071 222 9251

National Trust for Scotland
Friends of Greenbank Garden,
c/o Mrs Kathy Price, 23 Langtree
Avenue, Glasgow G46 7LJ
Tel: 041 638 7361

The Royal Association for Disability and Rehabilitation
(RADAR)
25 Mortimer St, London W1N 8AB
Tel: 071 637 5400

The Royal National Institute for the Blind
224 Great Portland Street, London W1N 6AA
Tel: 071 388 1266

Scottish Braille Press
Craigmillar Park, Edinburgh EH16 5NB
Tel: 031 667 0628

Scottish Council on Disability
Princes House, 5 Shandwick Place, Edinburgh EH2 4RG
Tel: 031 229 8632

Scottish National Federation for the Welfare of the Blind
8 St Leonards Bank, Perth, Perthshire PH2 8EB
Tel: 0738 26969

Society for Promotion of Rehabilitation in Gardening
(SPRIG)
c/o John Catlin, OT Dept, Dept of Psychiatry, Chase Farm Hospital, The Ridgeway, Enfield EN2 8JL
Tel: 081 366 6600

Southern & Western Regional Association for the Blind
55 Eton Avenue, London NW3 3ET
Tel: 071 722 9703

Spastics Society
12 Park Crescent, London N1N 4EQ
Tel: 071 636 5020

Talking Newspapers for the Blind
Browning Road, Heathfield TN21 8DB
Tel: 0435 866102

Wales Council for the Blind
Oak House, 12 The Bulwark, Brecon, Powys LD3 7AD
Tel: 0874 4576

Wales Council for the Disabled
Caerbragdy Industrial Estate, Bedwas Rd, Caerphilly, Mid Glamorgan CF8 3SL
Tel: 0222 869224

Plant Collections

The National Council for the Conservation of Plants and Gardens is an organization committed to conserving stocks of precious plants, especially those that may be at risk. To this end, their members have helped to establish an extraordinary number of collections.

The National Collections are held by organizations and individuals and are purely a labour of love. The collection holders often have a unique and detailed knowledge of their particular speciality which they're pleased to share with others and sometimes you can even buy the plants.

Some of the collections are in gardens open to the public and can be viewed whenever the gardens are open, but many are in private establishments. So, if you wish to visit, you may well need to write for an appointment. All are well worth the trouble.

The details of the collections are available in the *National Plant Collections Directory* which can be obtained from the following address.

National Council for the Conservation of Plants and Gardens
The Pines, Wisley Gardens, Woking, Surrey
Tel: (Guildford) 0483 211465

Gardens Open to the Public

There's no better way to get inspiration for your own garden than to visit other people's. Even the largest stately home gardens can inspire ideas for the tiniest plot. All you need to do is to scale them down. A garden visit is also a wonderful day out and a certain way to improve your gardening knowledge.

Fortunately, there's no country in the world better endowed with fine gardens open to the public than Britain. To list them all here would be impossible but any one of the following books and leaflets will provide the necessary information.

Blue Guide – Gardens of England
Written by: Frances Gapper, Patience Gapper and Sally Drury
Published by: A & C Black
Price £14.99

British Car Rental Guide to British Gardens
A free leaflet containing information of over 60 gardens obtainable from:
The British Travel Centre
12 Regent St, Piccadilly Circus, London SW1Y 4PQ

Gardens Handbook
Published by: The National Trust
36 Queen Anne's Gate, London SW1H 9AS
Price £3.95

Gardens of England & Wales (The Yellow Book)
Published by: The National Gardens Scheme
Hatchlands Park, East Clandon, Guildford, Surrey GU4 7RT
Price £2.00

The Gardeners' Guide to Britain
Written by: Patrick Taylor
Published by: Pavilion
Price £9.99

Good Gardens Guide
Edited by: Graham Rose and Peter King
Published by: Vermillion
Price £12.99

The Guide to over 100 Properties
Published by: The National Trust for Scotland
5 Charlotte Square, Edinburgh EH2 4DU
Price £1.00 (35p p&p)

The Shell Guide to the Gardens of England & Wales
Written by: Sarah Hollis and Derry Moore
Published by: Andre Deutsch
Price £17.95

Scotland's Garden
Published by: The Scotland Gardens Scheme
31 Castle Terrace, Edinburgh EH1 2EL
Price £2.00 (50p p&p)

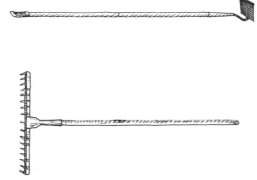

Specialist Nurseries

This country abounds with small and not-so-small specialist nurseries who are really the aristocrats of the industry. If you're interested in a particular genus or a certain type of plant, it's at such places that you'll find the widest range. It's important that we patronize the smaller specialists in particular, since their loss would make the gardening trade immeasurably poorer. Many of them make a fascinating day out too and you'll nearly always find someone there who's a *real* expert on the subject.

For further information and a huge range of nurseries, the Hardy Plant Society's *Plantfinder* is invaluable. You'll find it in most good bookshops.

Acacia
Celyn Vale Nurseries
Carrog, Corwen, Clwyd LL21 9LD

Acer
Hippopottering Nursery
Orchard House, Brackenhill Road,
Haxey, Nr Doncaster, North Yorkshire
DN9 2LR

P M A Plant Specialists
28 Essex Drive, Taunton, Somerset
TA1 4JY

Achimenes
Mr K J Townsend
17 Valerie Close, St Albans,
Hertfordshire AL1 5JD
Mail order only

Alpines
Ardfearn Nursery
Bunchrew, Inverness
IV3 6RH

Beechcroft Nursery
127 Reigate Road, Ewell, Surrey
KT17 3DE
No mail order

Blairhoyle Nursery
Port of Menteith, Stirling, Central
FK8 3LF
No mail order

Brambling House Alpines
119 Sheffield Road, Warmsworth,
Doncaster, South Yorkshire
DN4 9QX

Broadstone Alpines
13 The Nursery, High Street, Sutton
Courtenay, Abingdon, Oxfordshire
OX14 4UA

J M Burgess
Rectory Cottage, Sisland, Norwich,
Norfolk NR14 6EF
No mail order

Castle Alpines
Castle Road, Wootton, Woodstock,
Oxfordshire OX7 1EG

John Clayfield
Llanbrook Alpine Nursery, Hopton
Castle, Clunton, Shropshire
SY7 0QG

County Park Nursery
Essex Gardens, Hornchurch, Essex
RM11 3BU
No mail order

Jack Drake
Inshriach Alpine Nursery, Aviemore,
Invernesshire PH22 1QS

Field House Nurseries
Leake Road, Gotham, Nottingham
NG11 0JN

Hartside Nursery Garden
Nr Alston, Cumbria CA9 3BL

Highgates Nursery
166a Crich Lane, Belper, Derbyshire
DE5 1EP
No mail order

Hunters Oak Nursery
Bere Alston, Yelverton, Devon
PL20 7HT

Lewdon Farm Alpine Nursery
Medland Lane, Cheriton Bishop,
Nr Exeter, Devon EX6 6HF

Martin Nest Nurseries
Grange Cottage, Harpswell Lane,
Hemswell, Gainsborough, Lincolnshire
DN21 5UP

Newton Hill Alpines
335 Leeds Road, Newton Hill,
Wakefield, Yorkshire WF1 2JH

Nicky's Rock Garden Nursery
Broadhayes, Stockland, Honiton,
Devon EX14 9EH
No mail order

Norden Alpines
Hirst Road, Carlton, Nr Goole,
Humberside DN14 9PX
No mail order

The Old Manor Nursery
Twyning, Gloucester GL20 6DB

Pitts Farm Nursery
Shrewley, Warwick, Warwickshire
CV35 7BB

Potterton & Martin
The Cottage Nursery, Moortown
Road, Nettleton, Caistor, Lincolnshire
LN7 6HX

Rivendell Alpines
Horton Heath, Wimborne, Dorset
BH21 7JN

Ryal Nursery
East Farm Cottage, Ryal,
Northumberland NE20 0SA

Siskin Plants
April House, Davey Lane, Charsfield,
Woodbridge, Suffolk IP13 7QG

Southfarthing Alpines
Southfarthing, Hawkenbury,
Staplehurst, Kent TN12 0ED
No mail order

39 Steps
Grove Cottage, Forge Hill, Lydbrook,
Gloucestershire
GL17 9QS
No mail order

Thuya Alpine Nursery
Glebelands, Hartpury, Gloucestershire
GL19 3BW

West Kington Nurseries Ltd
Pound Hill, West Kington, Nr
Chippenham, Wiltshire SN14 7JG
No mail order

White Cottage Alpines
Eastgate, Rudston, Driffield, East
Yorkshire YO25 0UX

Alstroemeria
Steven Bailey
Silver Street, Sway, Lymington,
Hampshire SO41 6ZA

Aquatics
Bennett's Water Lily & Fish Farm
Putton Lane, Chickerell, Weymouth,
Dorset DT3 4AF

Blagdon Water Garden Centre Ltd
Bath Road, Upper Langford, Avon
BS18 7DN

Deanswood Plants
Potteries Lane, Littlethorpe, Ripon,
North Yorkshire HG4 3LG

Gardeners' World & English Water
Garden
Rock Lane, Washington, West Sussex
RH20 3BL

Higher End Nursery
Hale, Fordingbridge, Hampshire
SP6 2RA

Honeysome Aquatic Nursery
The Row, Sutton, Nr Ely,
Cambridgeshire CB6 2PF

Maydencroft Aquatic Nurseries
Maydencroft Lane, Gosmore, Hitchin,
Hertfordshire SG4 7QD

Reedley Nursery
Robinson Lane, Reedley, Brierfield,
Nr Nelson, Lancashire BB9 5QS

Rowden Gardens
Brentor, Nr Tavistock, Devon
PL19 0NG

Stapeley Water Gardens Ltd
London Road, Stapeley, Nantwich,
Cheshire CW5 7LH

The Water Garden Nursery
Highcroft, Moorend, Wembworthy,
Chumleigh, Devon EX18 7SG

Wildwoods Water Gardens Ltd
Theobalds Park Road, Crews Hill,
Enfield, Middlesex EN2 9BP

Aquilegia
John Drake
Hardwicke House, Fen Ditton,
Cambridgeshire CB5 8TF
Mail order only

Architectural Plants
Architectural Plants
Cooks Farm, Nuthurst, Horsham,
West Sussex RH13 6LH

Aster
Misses I Allen & J Huish
Quarry Farm, Wraxall, Bristol, Avon
BS19 1LE

Old Court Nurseries Ltd
Colwall, Nr Malvern, Worcestershire
WR13 6QE

Astilbe
Park Green Nurseries
Wetheringsett, Stowmarket, Suffolk
IP14 5QH

Auricula
Field House Nurseries
Leake Road, Gotham, Nottingham
NG11 0JN

Brenda Hyatt
1 Toddington Crescent, Bluebell Hill,
Chatham, Kent ME5 9QT

Azalea

Coghurst Nursery
Ivy House Lane, Near Three Oaks,
Hastings, East Sussex TN35 4NP

Exbury Enterprises Ltd
Exbury, Nr Southampton, Hampshire
SO4 1AZ

Glendoick Gardens Ltd
Perth PH2 7NS

Knaphill & Slocock Nurseries
Barrs Lane, Knaphill, Woking, Surrey
GU21 2JW

Lea Rhododendron Gardens Ltd
Lea, Matlock, Derbyshire DE4 5GH

Leonardslee Gardens
1 Mill Lane, Lower Beeding, West
Sussex RH13 6PX

Millais Nurseries
Crosswater Lane, Churt, Farnham,
Surrey GU10 2JN

F Morrey & Sons
Forest Nursery, Kelsall, Tarporley,
Cheshire CW6 0SW
No mail order

Pound Lane Nurseries
Ampfield, Nr Romsey, Hampshire
SO5 9BL

Wall Cottage Nursery
Lockengate, Bugle, St Austell,
Cornwall PL26 8RU

Whitehills Nurseries
Newton Stewart, Wigtownshire
DG8 6SL

Bamboo

Bamboo Nursery
Kingsgate Cottage, Wittersham,
Tenterden, Kent TN30 7NS

Drysdale Nursery
Bowerwood Road, Fordingbridge,
Hampshire SP6 1BN

Fulbrooke Nursery
43 Fulbrooke Road, Cambridgeshire
CB3 9EE

Jungle Giants
Plough Farm, Wigmore, Herefordshire
HR6 9UW

Begonias

Blackmore & Langdon Ltd
Pensford, Bristol, Avon BS18 4JL

Halsway Nursery
Halsway, Nr Crowcombe, Taunton,
Somerset TA4 4BB

Bonsai

Bromage & Young
St Mary's Gardens, Worplesdon,
Surrey GU3 3RS

Herons Bonsai Nursery
Wire Mill Lane, Newchapel, Nr
Lingfield, Surrey RH7 6HJ

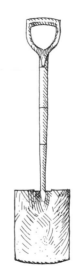

Samlesbury Bonsai Nursery
The Boat House, Potters Lane,
Samlesbury, Preston, Lancashire
PR5 0UE

Peter Trenear
Chantreyland, Chequers Lane,
Eversley Cross, Basingstoke,
Hampshire RG27 0NX

Bromeliads
Vesutor Ltd
The Bromeliad Nursery, Marringdean
Road, Billinghurst, West Sussex
RH14 9EH

Bulbs
Jacques Amand Ltd
The Nurseries, 145 Clamp Hill,
Stanmore, Middlesex HA7 3JS

Avon Bulbs
Burnt House Farm, Mid-Lambrook,
South Petherton, Somerset
TA13 5HE

Walter Blom & Son Ltd
Coombelands Nurseries, Leavesden,
Watford, Hertfordshire WD2 7BH

Rupert Bowlby
Gatton, Reigate, Surrey RH2 0TA

Broadleigh Gardens
Bishops Hull, Taunton, Somerset
TA4 1AE

Cambridge Bulbs
40 Whittlesford Road, Newton,
Cambridgeshire CB2 5PH

Paul Christian – Rare Plants
PO Box 468, Wrexham, Clwyd
LL13 9XR
Mail order only

Copford Bulbs
Dorsetts, Birch Road, Copford,
Colchester, Essex CO6 1DR

Knightshayes Garden Trust
The Garden Office, Knightshayes,
Tiverton, Devon EX16 7RG
No mail order

Frans Roozen (Holland)
c/o 34 Friars Road, Braughing, Ware,
Hertfordshire SG11 2NN

John Shipton (Bulbs)
Y Felin, Henllan Amgoed, Whitland,
Dyfed SA34 0SL

Van Tubergen UK Ltd
Bressingham, Diss, Norfolk
IP22 3AA
Mail order only

J Walkers Bulbs
Broadgate, Weston Hills, Spalding,
Lincolnshire PE12 6DQ
Mail order only

Buxus
Langley Boxwood Nursery
Langley Court, Rake, Liss, Hampshire
GU33 7JL

Cacti and Succulents
Bradley Batch Nursery
64 Bath Road, Bridgwater, Somerset
TA7 9QJ

Bridgemere Nurseries
Bridgemere, Cheshire CW5 7QB

Croston Cactus
43 Southport Road, Lancashire
PR7 6ET

Cruck Cottage Cacti
Cruck Cottage, Pickering, North
Yorkshire YO18 8PJ

East Midlands Cactus Nursery
Manor Close, Milton Keynes,
Buckinghamshire MK10 9AA

Eau Brink Cactus Nursery
Tilney, All Saints, Norfolk
PE34 4SQ

Felspar Cacti
20 Reawla Lane, Hayle, Cornwall
TR27 5HQ

W G Geissler
Winsford, Slimbridge, Gloucestershire
GL2 7BW

Glenhirst Cactus Nursery
Station Road, Nr Boston, Lincolnshire
PE20 3NX

Greenslacks Nurseries
Ocot Lane, Scammonden,
Huddersfield, Yorkshire HD3 3FR

Harvest Nurseries
Harvest Cottage, Iden, Sussex
TH31 7QA

Holly Gate Cactus Nursery
Billinghurst Lane, Ashington, West
Sussex RH20 3BA

Jumanery Cacti
St Catherine's Lodge, Whaplode St
Catherine, Lincolnshire PE12 6SR

K & C Cacti
Fern Cottage, Barnstaple, Devon
EX32 0SF

Kent Cacti
(Office) 35 Rutland Way,
Orpington, Kent BR5 4DY

Long Man Gardens
Lewes Road, Polgate, East Sussex
BN26 5RS

Mesa Gardens
32 Trafalgar Road, Southport,
Merseyside PR8 2EX

David Neville
17 Lupin Road, Southampton,
Hampshire SO2 3LD

Nutfield Nurseries
Crab Hill Lane, Surrey RH1 5PG

Oakleigh Nurseries
Petersfield Road, Nr Alresford,
Hampshire SO24 0HB

Pete & Ken Cactus Nursery
Saunders Lane, Nr Canterbury, Kent
CT3 2BX

A & A Phipps
62 Samuel White Road, Bristol
BS15 3LX

The Plant Lovers
Candesby House, Spilsby, Lincolnshire
PE23 5RU

Plantlife
32 Ramsey Way, East Sussex
BN23 6AL

Preston-Mafham Collection
2 Willoughby Close, Alcester,
Warwickshire B49 5QJ

Chris Rodgerson
35 Lydgate Hall Crescent, Sheffield,
South Yorkshire S10 5NE

Robert Scott
78 Bousley Rise, Surrey KT16 0LB

Southfield Nurseries
Louth Road, Grimsby, South
Humberside DN36 5HL

Toobees Nursery
20 Inglewood, Woking, Surrey
GU21 3HX

Westfield Cacti
Kennford, Devon EX6 7XD

Whitestone Gardens Ltd
The Cactus House, Thirsk, Yorkshire
YO7 2PZ

K M & R J R Willoughby
Willows Mead, Whittle-le-Woods,
Lancashire PR6 7DJ

H & J Wills
2 St Brannocks Park Road, Devon
EX34 8HU

Roy Young Seeds
23 Westland Chase, King's Lynn,
Norfolk PE33 0QH

Camellias
Ard Daraich Shrub Nursery
Ardgour, by Fort William,
Invernesshire PH33 7AB
No mail order

Bodnant Gardens
Tal-y-Cafn, Colwyn Bay, North Wales
LL28 5RE

Coghurst Nursery
Ivy House Lane, Near Three Oaks,
Hastings, East Sussex TN35 4NP

Exbury Enterprises Ltd
Exbury, Nr Southampton, Hampshire
SO4 1AZ

Porthpean House Gardens
Porthpean, St Austell, Cornwall
PL26 6AX

Trehane Camellias
Camellia Nursery, Stapehill Road,
Hampreston, Wimborne, Dorset
BH21 7NE

Trewidden Estate Nursery
Trewidden Gardens, Penzance,
Cornwall TR20 8TT

Trewithen Nurseries
Grampound Road, Truro, Cornwall
TR2 4DD

Campanula
Padlock Croft
19 Padlock Road, West Wratting,
Cambridgeshire CB1 5LS

Shrewley Gardens
Crossways, Shrewley, Nr Warwick,
Warwickshire CV35 7AU
Mail order only

Carnations
Steven Bailey
Silver Street, Sway, Lymington,
Hampshire SO41 6ZA

Haywards Carnations
The Chace Gardens, Stakes Road,
Purbrook, Portsmouth, Hampshire
PO7 5PL

Woodfield Bros
Wood End, Clifford Chambers,
Stratford-on-Avon, Warwickshire
CV37 8HR

Carnivorous Plants
Marston Exotics
Brampton Lane, Madley,
Herefordshire HR2 9LX

Plantcraft
(Office) 35 Rutland Way, Orpington,
Kent BR5 4DY

Potterton & Martin
The Cottage Nursery, Moortown
Road, Nettleton, Caistor, Lincolnshire
LN7 6HX

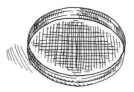

Chamomile
Morehavens
28 Denham Lane, Gerrards Cross,
Buckinghamshire SL9 0EX

Mrs M Warwick
Lower Trenode, Widegates, Looe,
Cornwall PL13 1QA

Chrysanthemum
Collinwood Nurseries
Mottram St Andrew, Macclesfield,
Cheshire SK10 4QR

Halls of Heddon
(Office) West Heddon Nurseries,
Heddon-on-the-Wall, Newcastle-upon-
Tyne NE15 0JS

Riley's Chrysanthemums
Alfreton Nurseries, Woolley Moor,
Derbyshire DE5 6FF

The Useful Plant Company
3 Church Street, Buckden,
Huntingdon, Cambridgeshire
PE18 9TE

H Woolman Ltd
Grange Road, Dorridge, Solihull, West
Midlands B93 8QB

Clematis
John Beach (Nursery) Ltd
(Office) 9 Grange Road,
Wellesbourne, Warwickshire
CV35 9RL

Bennett & Brown (Clematis)
Stoney Lane, Beamish, Co Durham
DH9 0SJ
No mail order

Caddick's Clematis Nurseries
Dyer's Lane, Rushgreen Road, Lymm,
Cheshire WA13 9QL

Fisk's Clematis Nursery
Westleton, Saxmundham, Suffolk
IP17 3AJ

Glyndley Nurseries
Hailsham Road, Pevensey, East Sussex
BN24 5BS
Mail order only

M Oviatt-Ham
(Office) Ely House, 15 Green Street,
Willingham, Cambridgeshire
CB4 5JA

Peveril Clematis Nursery
Christow, Exeter, Devon EX6 7NG
No mail order

Priorswood Clematis
Priorswood, Widbury Hill, Ware,
Hertfordshire SG12 7QH

Sherston Parva Nursery
21 Court Street, Sherston, Wiltshire
SN16 0LL
No mail order

Treasures of Tenbury Ltd
Burford House Gardens, Tenbury
Wells, Worcestershire WR15 8HQ

The Valley Clematis Nursery
Willingham Road, Hainton,
Lincolnshire LN3 6LN

Coleus
Halsway Nursery
Halsway, Nr Crowcombe, Taunton,
Somerset TA4 4BB

Conifers
Barncroft Nurseries
Dunwood Lane, Longsdon, Nr Leek,
Stoke-on-Trent, Staffordshire
ST9 9QW
No mail order

Beechcroft Nursery
127 Reigate Road, Ewell, Surrey
KT17 3DE
No mail order

The Conifer Garden
Saltway Farm, Northleach,
Gloucestershire GL54 3QB
No mail order

Crail Nurseries Ltd
Newstead Abbey Park, Nottingham
NG15 8GD
No mail order

Kenwith Nursery (Gordon Haddow)
The Old Rectory, Littleham, Bideford,
North Devon EX39 5HW

Lime Cross Nursery
Herstmonceux, Hailsman, East Sussex
BN27 4RS
No mail order

Lincluden Nursery
Bisley Green, Bisley, Woking, Surrey
GU24 9EN
No mail order

Norwich Heather & Conifer Centre
54a Yarmouth Road, Thorpe,
Norwich, Norfolk NR14 6PU

Conservatory Plants
Abbott's House Garden
10 High Street, Abbots Langley,
Hertfordshire WD5 0AR

B & H M Baker
Bourne Brook Nurseries, Greenstead
Green, Halstead, Essex CO9 1RJ
No mail order

Chessington Nurseries Ltd
Leatherhead Road, Chessington,
Surrey KT9 2NF

Deelish Garden Centre
Skibbereen, Co. Cork, Eire

Hardy Exotics
Trebah Gardens, Trebah, Mawnan
Smith, Falmouth, Cornwall
TR11 5JZ

Hill House Nursery & Gardens
Landscove, Nr Ashburton, Devon
TQ13 7LY
No mail order

Long Man Gardens
Lewes Road, Wilmington, Polegate,
East Sussex BN26 5RS

Lower Severalls Herb Nursery
Crewkerne, Somerset TA18 7NX

Newington Nursery
Newington, Wallingford, Oxfordshire
OX10 7AW

Pleasant View Nursery
Two Mile Oak, Nr Denbury, Newton
Abbot, Devon TQ12 6DG

Reads Nursery
Hales Hall, Loddon, Norfolk
NR14 6QW

Clive Simms
Woodhurst, Essendine, Stamford,
Lincolnshire PE9 4LQ

Sunbeam Nurseries
Bristol Road, Frampton Cotterell,
Avon BS17 2AU

Westdale Nurseries
Holt Road, Bradford-on-Avon,
Wiltshire BA15 1TS

Convallaria
Special Plants
Laurels Farm, Upper Wraxall,
Chippenham, Wiltshire SN14 7AG

John Sinden
10 Derwent Water Road, Merley
Ways, Wimbourne, Dorset
BH21 1QS

Cordyline
The Torbay Pal Farm
St Marychurch Road, Coffinswell, Nr
Newton Abbot, Devon TQ12 4SE

Cornus
Royal Horticultural Society's Garden
Rosemoor, Great Torrington, Devon
EX38 8PH
No mail order

Crambe
A R Paske
The South Lodge, Gazeley Road,
Kentford, Newmarket, Suffolk
CB8 7QA

Cyclamen
Little Creek Nursery
39 Moor Road, Banwell, Weston-
super-Mare, Avon BS24 6EF

Tile Barn Nursery
Standen Street, Iden Green,
Benenden, Kent TN17 4LB

Daffodils
Ballydorn Bulb Farm
Killinchy, Newtownards, Co Down, N
Ireland BT23 6QB
Mail order only

J Walkers Bulbs
Broadgate, Weston Hills, Spalding,
Lincolnshire PE12 6DQ
Mail order only

Dahlias
Tom Bebbington Dahlias
Lady Gate Nursery, 47 The Green,
Diseworth, Derbyshire DE7 2QN

Ian Butterfield
Butterfields Nursery, Harvest Hill,
Bourne End, Buckinghamshire
SL8 5JJ

Halls of Heddon
(Office) West Heddon Nurseries,
Heddon-on-the-Wall, Newcastle-upon-
Tyne NE15 0JS

Oscroft's Dahlias
'Woodside', Warwick Road, Chadwick
End, Nr Solihull, West Midlands
B93 0BP
and
Sportbro' Road, Doncaster, South
Yorkshire DN5 8BE

Philip Tivey & Son
28 Wanlip Road, Syston, Leicestershire
LE7 8PA

Delphinium
Blackmore & Langdon
Pensford, Bristol, Avon BS18 4JL

Harrisons Delphiniums
Newbury Cottage, Play Hatch,
Reading, Berkshire RG4 9QN

Stuart Ogg
Hopton, Fletching Street, Mayfield,
East Sussex TN20 6TL

Woodfield Bros
Wood End, Clifford Chambers,
Stratford-on-Avon, Warwickshire
CV37 8HR

Erodium
Charter House Nursery
2 Nunwood, Stepford Road, Dumfries
& Galloway DG2 7RE

Eucalyptus
Celyn Vale Nurseries
Carrog, Corwen, Clwyd LL21 9LD

Liscahane Nursery
Ardfert, Tralee, Co. Kerry, Eire

Euphorbia
Farmhouse Plants
Royal Farm House, Elstead,
Godalming, Surrey GU8 6LA
No mail order

Ferns
Fibrex Nurseries Ltd
Honeybourne Road, Pebworth,
Stratford-on-Avon, Warwickshire
CV37 8XT

J & D Marston
Culag, Green Lane, Nafferton,
Driffield, East Yorkshire YO25 0LF

Fuchsia
B & H M Baker
Bourne Brook Nurseries, Greenstead
Green, Halstead, Essex CO9 1RJ
No mail order

R J Blythe
Potash Nursery, Cow Green, Bacton,
Stowmarket, Suffolk IP14 4HJ

Goulding's Fuchsias
West View, Link Lane, Bentley, Nr
Ipswich, Suffolk IP9 2DP

Jackson's Nurseries
Clifton Campville, Nr Tamworth,
Staffordshire B79 0AP

Laburnum Nurseries
c/o 6 Manor House Gardens, Main
Street, Humberstone Village,
Leicestershire LE5 1AE

Little Brook Fuchsias
Ash Green Lane West, Ash Green, Nr
Aldershot, Hampshire
GU12 6HL
No mail order

C S Lockyer
Lansbury, 70 Henfield Road, Coalpit
Heath, Bristol, Avon BS17 2UZ

Markham Grange Nurseries
Long Lands Lane, Brodsworth, Nr
Doncaster, South Yorkshire DN5 7XB

Kathleen Muncaster Fuchsias
18 Field Lane, Morton, Gainsborough,
Lincolnshire DN21 3BY

Oakleigh Nurseries
Monkwood, Alresford, Hampshire
SO24 0HB

Oldbury Nurseries
Brissenden Green, Bethersden, Kent
TN26 3BJ
No mail order

Orange's Nursery
Oakdene, Newby East, Carlisle,
Cumbria CA4 8QX

Paul's Fuchsias
Gors Farm, Rhydargaeau,
Carmarthen, Gwynedd SA32 7AP

Pendennis Fuchsia Nursery
14 Pendennis Road, Heaton Norris,
Stockport, Cheshire SK4 2QA

J V Porter
12 Hazel Grove, Southport,
Merseyside PR8 6AX

John Smith & Son
Hilltop Nurseries, Thornton,
Leicestershire LE6 1AN

A P & E V Tabraham
Porth Mellon, St Mary's, Isles of Scilly
TR21 0JY

Ward Fuchsias
5 Pollen Close, Sale, Cheshire
M33 3LP

Galanthus
John Morley
North Green Only, Stoven, Beccles,
Suffolk NR34 8DG
Mail order only

Gentians
Angus Heathers
10 Guthrie Street, Letham, Forfar,
Tayside DD8 2PS
No mail order

Geraniums
Catforth Gardens
Roots Lane, Catforth, Preston,
Lancashire PR4 0JB
No mail order

Francis Mount Perennial Plants
1 Steps Farm, Polstead, Colchester,
Essex CO6 5AE

Hosford's Geraniums & Garden
Centre
Cappa, Enniskeane, Co. Cork, Eire

Pearl Sulman
54 Kingsway, Mildenhall, Bury St
Edmunds, Suffolk IP28 7HR
Mail order only

The Vernon Geranium Nursery
Cuddington Way, Cheam, Sutton,
Surrey SM2 7JB

Grasses
Farmhouse Plants
Royal Farm House, Elstead,
Godalming, Surrey GU8 6LA
No mail order

Hoecroft Plants
Severals Grange, Wood Norton,
Dereham, Norfolk NR20 5BL

Lesley Marshall
Islington Lodge Cottage, Tilney All
Saints, King's Lynn, Norfolk
PE34 4SF

Trevor Scott
Thorpe Park Cottage, Thorpe-le-
Soken, Essex CO16 0HN

Heathers
Angus Heathers
10 Guthrie Street, Letham, Forfar,
Tayside DD8 2PS
No mail order

Barncroft Nurseries
Dunwood Lane, Longsdon, Nr Leek,
Stoke-on-Trent, Staffordshire
ST9 9QW
No mail order

Blairhoyle Nursery
Port of Menteith, Stirling, Central
FK8 3LF
No mail order

Crail Nurseries Ltd
Newstead Abbey Park, Nottingham
NG15 8GD
No mail order

Denbeigh Heather Nurseries
All Saints Road, Creeting St Mary,
Ipswich, Suffolk IP6 8PJ

M G Frye
'The Willows', Poors Lane North,
Daws Heath, Thundersley, Essex
SS7 2XF

Greenacres Nursery
Bringsty, Worcestershire WR6 5TA
No mail order

The Heather Garden
139 Swinston Hill Road, Dinnington,
Sheffield, South Yorkshire S31 7RY

Herb & Heather Centre
West Haddlesey, Nr Selby, North
Yorkshire YO8 8QA

Naked Cross Nurseries
Waterloo Road, Corfe Mullen,
Wimborne, Dorset BH21 3SR
No mail order

Norwich Heather & Conifer Centre
54a Yarmouth Road, Thorpe,
Norwich, Norfolk NR14 6PU

Okell's Nurseries
Duddon Heath, Nr Tarporley,
Cheshire CW6 0EP

Otters' Court Heathers
Otters' Court, West Camel, Yeovil,
Somerset BA22 7QF

Pennyacre Nurseries
Station Road, Springfield, Fife
KY15 5RU

Ridgeway Heather Nursery
Park House, Plaish, Church Stretton,
Salop SY6 7HY
No mail order

Speyside Heather Garden Centre
Dulnain Bridge, Highland PH26 3PA

Wingates
62A Chorley Road, Westhoughton,
Bolton, Lancashire BL5 3PL
No mail order

Hedera
Fibrex Nurseries Ltd
Honeybourne Road, Pebworth,
Stratford-on-Avon, Warwickshire
CV37 8XT
No mail order

Whitehouse Ivies
Hylands Farm, Rectory Road,
Tolleshunt Knights, Maldon, Essex
CM9 8EZ

Hellebores
Helen Ballard
Old Country, Mathon, Malvern,
Hereford & Worcester WR13 5PS

Fibrex Nurseries Ltd
Honeybourne Road, Pebworth, Nr
Stratford-on-Avon, Warwickshire
CV37 8XT
No mail order

Little Creek Nursery
39 Moor Road, Banwell, Weston-
super-Mare, Avon BS24 6EF

Phedar Nursery
Bunkers Hill, Romily, Stockport,
Cheshire SK6 3DS

Washfield Nursery
Horn's Road, Hawkhurst, Kent
TN18 4QU

Herbs
Arne Herbs
Limeburn Nurseries, Limeburn Hill,
Chew Magna, Avon BS18 8QW

Billy's Herbs
Manor Farm, Stradbroke, Diss,
Norfolk IP21 5NJ

Candlesby Herbs
Cross Keys, Candlesby, Lincolnshire
PE23 5SF

Cheshire Herbs
Fourfields, Forest Hill, Little
Budworth, Cheshire CW6 9ES

The Cottage Herbery
Mill House, Boraston Ford, Boraston,
Nr Tenbury Wells, Hereford &
Worcester WR15 8LZ

Cowcombe Farm Herbs
Gipsy Lane, Chalford, Stroud,
Gloucestershire GL6 8HP

Daphne Ffiske Herbs
Rosemary Cottage, Bramerton,
Norwich, Norfolk N14 7DW

Devon Herbs
Burn Lane, Brentor, Tavistock, Devon
PL19 0ND

Eden Plants
Eden, Rossinver, Co. Leitrum, Eire

Elly Hill Herbs
Elly Hill House, Brampton,
Darlington, Durham DL1 3JF

Elsworth Herbs
Avenue Farm Cottage, 31 Smith
Street, Elsworth, Cambridgeshire
CB3 8IIY

Fold Garden
26 Fold Lane, Biddulph, Staffordshire
ST8 7SG

Herb & Heather Centre
West Haddlesey, Nr Selby, North
Yorkshire YO8 8QA

The Herbary Plant Centre
89 Station Road, Herne Bay, Kent
CT6 5QQ
No mail order

The Herb Farm
Peppard Road, Sonning Common,
Reading, Berkshire RG4 9NJ

The Herb Garden
Plant Hunter's Nursery, Capel Ulo,
Pentre Berw, Gaerwen, Anglesey,
Gwynedd LL60 6LF

The Herb Nursery
Grange Farm, Main Street, Thistleton,
Rutland LE15 7RE

Hexham Herbs
Chesters Walled Garden, Chollerford,
Hexham, Northumberland NE46 4BQ
No mail order

Hill Farm Herbs
Park Walk, Brigstock, Kettering,
Northamptonshire NN14 3HH

Caroline Holmes
Denham End Farm, Denham, Bury St
Edmunds, Suffolk IP29 5EE

Hunters Oak Nursery
Bere, Alston, Yelverton, Devon
PL20 7HT

Iden Croft Herbs
Frittenden Road, Staplehurst, Kent
TN12 0DH

Lisdoonan Herbs
98 Belfast Road, Saintfield, Co. Down,
Northern Ireland BT24 7HF
No mail order

Lower Severells Herb Nursery
Crewkerne, Somerset TA18 7NX

Marle Place Plants and Gardens
Marle Place, Brenchley, Nr Tonbridge,
Kent TN12 7HS

Netherfields Herbs
37 Nether Street, Rougham, Nr Bury
St Edmunds, Suffolk IP30 9LW

Oak Cottage Herb Garden
Nesscliffe, Nr Shrewsbury, Salop
SY4 1DB

The Old Mill Herbery
Helland Bridge, Bodmin, Cornwall
PL30 4QR

Parkinson Herbs
Barras Moor Farm, Perran-ar-Worthal,
Truro, Cornwall TR3 7PE

Poyntzfield Herb Nursery
Nr Balblair, Black Isle, Dingwall, Ross
& Cromarty, Highland
IV7 8LX

Scotland Farmhouse Herbs
Virginstow, Beaworthy, Devon
EX21 5AE

Sellet Hall Herbs
Whittington, via Carnforth, Lancashire
LA6 2QF

Westhall Herbs
Church Lane, Westhall, Nr
Halesworth, Suffolk IP19 8NU

Wye Valley Herbs
The Nurtons, Tinerton, Chepstow,
Gwent NP6 7NX

Hosta
Ann & Roger Bowden
Cleave House, Sticklepath,
Okehampton, Devon EX20 2NN

Goldbrook Plants
Hoxne, Eye, Suffolk IP21 5AN

Kittoch Plants
Kittoch Mill, Busby Road,
Carmunnock, Glasgow, Strathclyde
G76 9BJ

Mickfield Market Garden
The Poplars, Mickfield, Stowmarket,
Suffolk IP14 5LH

Insectivorous Plants
Steventon Road Nurseries
Steventon Road, East Hanney,
Wantage, Oxfordshire OX12 OHS
No mail order

Iris
Croftway Nursery
Yapton Road, Barnham, Bognor
Regis, West Sussex PO22 0BH

V H Humphrey – Iris Specialist
Westlees Farm, Logmore Lane,
Westcott, Dorking, Surrey RH4 3JN

Zephyrwude Irises
48 Blacker Lane, Crigglestone,
Wakefield, West Yorkshire
WF4 3EW
Mail order only

Ivy – *see* **Hedera**

Lavandula
Jersey Lavender Ltd
Rue du Pont Marquet, St Brelade,
Jersey, Channel Islands JE3 8DS
No mail order

Norfolk Lavender
Caley Hill, Heacham, King's Lynn,
Norfolk PE31 7JE

Lewisia
Ashwood Nurseries
Greenforge, Kingswinford, West
Midlands DY6 0AE

Brynbyfryd Nurseries
Rhydycrorsan, Nr Oswestry,
Shropshire SY10 7JF

Liliaceae
Walter Blom and Son Ltd
Coombelands Nurseries, Leavesdon,
Watford, Hertfordshire WD2 7BH

Bullwood Nursery
54 Woodlands Road, Hockley, Essex
SS5 4PY

J Walkers Bulbs
Broadgate, Weston Hills, Spalding,
Lincolnshire PE12 6DQ
Mail order only

Lupins
Woodfield Bros
Wood End, Clifford Chambers,
Stratford-on-Avon, Warwickshire
CV37 8HR

Magnolia
Bodnant Garden Nursery Ltd
Tal-y-Catn, Colwyn Bay, North Wales
LL28 5RE

Meconopsis
Craigieburn Classic Plants
Craigieburn House, by Moffat,
Dumfriesshire DG10 9LF

Lingholm Gardens
Lingholm, Keswick, Cumbria
CA12 5UA
No mail order

Narcissus
Walter Blom and Son Ltd
Coombelands Nurseries, Leavesden,
Watford, Hertfordshire WD2 7BH

Carncairn Daffodils
Broughshane, Ballymena, Co. Antrim,
Northern Ireland BT43 7HF

Brian Duncan
Novelty & Exhibition Daffodils
15 Ballnahatty Road, Omagh, Co.
Tyrone, Northern Ireland BT78 1PN

Evelic Daffodils
Aird Asaig, Evelix, Dornoch,
Sutherland IV25 3NG

Orchids
Burnham Nurseries
Forches Cross, Devon TQ12 6PZ

Deva Orchids
Littlebrook Farm, Pen-y-fford, Chester
CH4 0JY

Greenway Orchids
Rookery Farm, Nr Weston-super-
Mare, Avon BS24 6TL

Mansell & Hatcher Ltd
Cragg Wood Nurseries, Rawdon,
Leeds LS19 6LQ

McBeans Orchids Ltd
Cooksbridge, Sussex BN8 4PR

Orchid Sundries Ltd
New Gate Farm, Gillingham, Dorset
SP8 5LT

Stonehurst Nurseries
Stonehurst, Ardingly, Sussex
RH17 6TN

Thatched Lodge Orchids
Millhayes, Honiton, Devon
EX14 9DE

Westwood Nursery
65 Yorkland Avenue, Kent
DA16 2LE
Mail order only

Woodstock Orchids
Woodstock House, Great Brickhill,
Buckinghamshire MK17 9AS

Palms
The Palm Centre
563 Upper Richmond Road West,
London SW14 7ED

The Palm Farm
Thornton Hall Gardens, Station Road,
Thornton Curtis, Nr Ulceby,
Humberside DN39 6XF

Passiflora
Greenholm Nurseries
(Office) Lampley Road, Kingston
Seymour, Clevedon, Avon BS21 6XS

Pelargonium
Denmead Geranium Nurseries
Hambledon Road, Denmead,
Waterlooville, Hampshire PO7 6PS

Fibrex Nurseries Ltd
Honeybourne Road, Pebworth,
Stratford-on-Avon, Warwickshire
CV37 8XT
No mail order

Jarvis Brook Geranium Nurseries
Tubwell Lane, Jarvis Brook,
Crowborough, Sussex TN6 3RH

Derek Lloyd Dean
8 Lynwood Close, South Harrow,
Middlesex HA2 9PR
Mail order only

Oakleigh Nurseries
Monkwood, Alresford, Hampshire
SO24 0HB

The Vernon Geranium Nursery
Cuddington Way, Cheam, Sutton,
Surrey SM2 7JB

A D & N Wheeler
Pye Court, Willoughby, Rugby,
Warwickshire CV23 8BZ

Phlox
Blackmore & Langdon Ltd
Pensford, Bristol, Avon BS18 4JL

Pieris
The High Garden
Courtwood, Newton Ferrers, Devon
PL8 1BW

Pinks
Allwood Bros
Mill Nursery, Hassocks, West Sussex
BN6 9NB

Haywards Carnations
The Chace Gardens, Stakes Road,
Purbrook, Portsmouth, Hampshire
PO7 5PL

Kingstone Cottage Plants
Weston-under-Penyard, Ross-on-Wye,
Herefordshire HR9 7NX

Mill Cottage Plants
The Mill, Henley Lane, Wookey,
Somerset BA5 1AP

Mills' Farm Plants & Gardens
Norwich Road, Mendlesham, Suffolk
IP14 5NQ

Pinks & Carnations
22 Chetwyn Avenue, Bromley Cross,
Bolton, Lancashire BL7 9BN

Southview Nurseries
Chequers Lane, Eversley Cross,
Basingstoke, Hampshire RG27 0NT

Three Counties Nurseries
Marshwood, Bridport, Dorset
DT6 5QJ
Mail order only

Pleiones
Ian Butterfield
Butterfields Nursery, Harvest Hill,
Bourne End, Buckinghamshire
SL8 5JJ

Westwood Nursery
65 Yorkland Avenue, Welling, Kent
DA16 2LE
Mail order only

Primula
Cottage Garden Plants Old & New
Cox Cottage, Lower Street, East
Norden, Wareham, Dorset
BH20 7DL

Craigieburn Classic Plants
Craigieburn House, by Moffat,
Dumfriesshire DG10 9LF

Field House Nurseries
Leake Road, Gotham, Nottingham
NG11 0JN

Lingholm Gardens
Lingholm, Keswick, Cumbria
CA12 5UA
No mail order

Mrs Ann Lunn
The Fens, Old Mill Road, Langham,
Colchester, Essex CO4 5NU

Pulmonaria
Stillingfleet Lodge Nurseries
Stillingfleet, Yorkshire YO4 6HW

Rhododendrons
Ard Daraich Shrub Nursery
Ardgour, By Fort William,
Invernesshire PH33 7AB
No mail order

Ballalheannagh Gardens
Glen Roy, Lonan, Isle of Man

Bodnant Garden Nursery Ltd
Tal-y-Cafn, Colwyn Bay, North Wales
LL28 5RE

Coghurst Nursery
Ivy House Lane, Near Three Oaks,
Hastings, East Sussex TN35 4NP

Exbury Enterprises Ltd
Exbury, Near Southampton,
Hampshire SO4 1AZ

Glendoick Gardens Ltd
Perth PH2 7NS

The High Garden
Courtswood, Newton Ferrers, South
Devon PL8 1BW

Hydon Nurseries Ltd
Clock Barn Lane, Hydon Heath,
Godalming, Surrey GU8 4AZ

Knaphill & Slocock Nurseries
Barrs Lane, Knaphill, Woking, Surrey
GU21 2JW

Lea Rhodondendron Gardens Ltd
Lea, Matlock, Derbyshire DE4 5GH

Leonardslee Gardens
1 Mill Lane, Lower Beeding, West
Sussex RH13 6PX

Millais Nurseries
Crosswater Lane, Churt, Farnham,
Surrey GU10 2JN

F Morrey & Sons
Forest Nursery, Kelsall, Tarporley,
Cheshire CW6 0SW
No mail order

Pound Lane Nurseries
Ampfield, Nr Romsey, Hampshire
SO5 9BL

Trewithen Nurseries
Grampound Road, Truro, Cornwall
TR2 4DD

Wall Cottage Nursery
Lockengate, Bugle, St Austell,
Cornwall PL26 8RU

Whitehills Nurseries
Newton Stewart, Wigtownshire,
Scotland DG8 6SL

Roses
Abbey Rose Gardens
Burnham, Buckinghamshire SL1 8NJ

Acton Beauchamp Roses
Nr Worcester WR6 5AE

Anderson's Rose Nurseries
Friarsfield Road, Cults, Aberdeen
AB1 9QT

Apuldram Roses
Apuldram Lane, Dell Quay,
Chichester, West Sussex PO20 7EF

David Austin Roses
Bowling Green Lane, Albrighton,
Wolverhampton, Staffordshire
WV7 3HB

Battersby Roses
Pear Tree Cottage, Old Battersby,
Great Ayton, Cleveland TS9 6LU

Peter Beales Roses
London Road, Attleborough, Norfolk
NR17 1AY

Walter Bentley & Sons Ltd
The Nurseries, Loughborough Road,
Wanlip, Leicester LE7 8PN

Bowood Garden Centre
Bowood Estate, Calne, Wiltshire
SN11 0LZ
No mail order

Brannel Farm Roses
Brannel Farm, St Stephens, Coombe,
St Austell, Cornwall PL25 7LG

Brokenbacks Roses
Broxhill Road, Havering-atte-Bower,
Romford, Essex RM4 1QH

Burrows Roses
Meadow Croft, Spondon Road, Dale
Abbey, Derbyshire DE7 4PQ
Mail order only

Cants of Colchester Ltd
Nayland Road, Mile End, Colchester
CO4 5EB

John Charles Nurseries Ltd
64 Derby Road, Risley, Derbyshire
DE7 3SU

Paul Chessum
21 High Street, Great Barford,
Bedford MK44 3JH

Chichester Roses Ltd
Chalder Farm, Sidlesham, Chichester,
West Sussex PO20 7RN

Cley Nurseries
Holt Road, Cley-Next-The-Sea, Holt,
Norfolk NR25 7TX

James Cocker & Sons
Whitemyres, Lang Stracht, Aberdeen
AB9 2XH

W H Collin & Sons (Roses) Ltd
The Manor House, Knossington,
Oakham, Leicestershire LE15 8LX

Cottage Garden Roses
Woodlands House, Stretton, Nr
Stafford ST19 9LG

D & W Croll Ltd
Dalhouse Nurseries, Broughty Ferry,
Dundee DD5 2PP

Peter Delves Rose Grower
Woolhouse Nursery, Redford,
Midhurst, Sussex GU29 0QH

Dickson Nurseries Ltd
Milecross Road, Newtownards, Co.
Down, Northern Ireland BT23 4SS

Doubleday & Co
Walnut Hill, Surlingham, Norwich,
Norfolk NR14 7DQ

English Cottage Roses Ltd
The Nurseries, Stapleford Lane,
Toton, Beeston, Nottinghamshire
NG9 5FD

Leo Esser & Son
Grange Farm Nursery, Barton Road
(B1441), Wisbech, Cambridgeshire
PE13 4TH

Fryer's Nurseries Ltd
Knutsford, Cheshire WA16 0SX

Gandy's Roses Ltd
North Kilworth, Nr Lutterworth,
Leicestershire LE17 6HZ

Godly's Roses
Dunstable Road, Redbourn, St
Albans, Hertfordshire AL3 7PS

Greenhead Roses
Greenhead Nursery, Old Greenock
Road, Inchinnan, Renfrew, Strathclyde
PA4 9PH

Handley Rose Nurseries
Lightwood Road, Marsh Lane, Nr
Sheffield S31 9RG

Hadspen Garden & Nursery
Hadspen House, Castle Cary,
Somerset BA7 7NG
No mail order

R Harkness & Co Ltd
The Rose Gardens, Hitchin,
Hertfordshire SG4 0JT

F Haynes & Partners Ltd
(Office) 56 Gordon Street, Kettering,
Northamptonshire NN16 0RX

Highfield Nurseries
Whitminster, Gloucestershire GL2 7PL

Hill Park Nurseries
Kingston by pass, Surbiton, Surrey
KT6 5HN

Hockenhull Roses
28 Hallfields Road, Tarvin, Chester
CH3 8LL

Hunts Court Garden & Nursery
North Nibley, Dursley, Gloucestershire
GL11 8DZ

C & K Jones (Rose Specialists)
Golden Fields Nursery,
Gloucestershire GL11 8DZ

Just Roses
Beales Lane, Northiam, Nr Rye, East
Sussex TN31 6QY

Layham Nurseries & Garden Centre
Summerfield, Staple, Canterbury, Kent
CT3 1LD

LeGrice Roses
Norwich Road, North Walsham,
Norfolk NR28 0DR

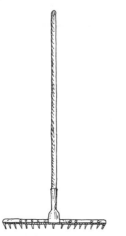

The Limes New Roses
Kerry, Lifton, Devon PL16 0HQ

Mattock's Roses
The Rose Nurseries, Nuneham
Courtenay, Oxfordshire OX9 9PY

Nottcutts Nurseries Ltd
Woodbridge, Suffolk IP12 4AF

O K Roses
Ferriby High Road, North Ferriby,
North Humberside HU14 3LA

A J Palmer & Son
Denham Court Nursery, Village Road,
Denham, Uxbridge, Middlesex
UB9 5BQ

Pennine Nurseries
Shelley, Huddersfield HD8 8LG

J B Philp & Son Ltd
Elm Park Garden Centre, Pamber
End, Basingstoke, Hampshire
RG26 5QW

Pocock's Nurseries
Dandys Ford Lane, Sherfield English,
Romsey, Hampshire SO51 6FT

Rearsby Roses
Melton Road, Rearsby, Leicestershire
LE7 8YP

Redhill Roses
Thurlby Farm, Thurlby Lane, Stanton-
on-the-Wolds, Nottinghamshire
NG12 5PL

R V Roger Ltd
The Nurseries, Pickering, North
Yorkshire YO18 7HG

Roses & Shrubs Garden Centre
Newport Road, Albrighton, Nr
Wolverhampton, West Midlands
WV7 3ER

Rosslow Roses
North Street Farm, North Street,
Hellingly, Hailsham, East Sussex
BN27 4DZ

Andrew de Ruiter (Rose Specialist)
9 Ingersley Road, Bollington, Cheshire
SK10 5RE
Mail order only

Rumwood Nurseries
Langley, Maidstone, Kent ME17 3ND

John Sanday (Roses) Ltd
Over Lane, Almondsbury, Bristol,
Avon BS12 4DA

Shaw Rose Trees
2 Hollowgate Hill, Willoughton,
Gainsborough, Lincolnshire
DN21 5SF

Slacks Roses
White Post, Farnsfield,
Nottinghamshire NG22 8HZ

St Bridget Nurseries Ltd
Old Rydon Lane, Exeter, Devon
EX2 7JY

J A Steele & Sons Ltd
The Market Place, Regent Street,
Newtownards, County Down,
Northern Ireland

Henry Street
Swallowfield Road Nursery,
Arborfield, Reading, Berkshire
RG2 9JY

Stydd Nursery
Stonygate Lane, Ribchester, Nr
Preston, Lancashire PR3 3YN

Sussex County Gardens
Newhaven Road, Kingston, Nr Lewes,
East Sussex BN7 3NE
No mail order

Timmermans Roses
Lowdham Lane, Woodborough,
Nottinghamshire NG14 6DN

John Train & Sons
Benston, Tarbolton, Strathclyde
KA5 5NT

L W Van Geest (Farms) Ltd
Wool Hall Farm, Wykeham, Spalding,
Lincolnshire PE12 6HW

Warley Rose Gardens Ltd
Warley Street, Great Warley,
Brentwood, Essex CM13 3JH

F & G F Webb
Orchard Nurseries, 90 Peters Point,
Sutton Bridge, Spalding, Lincolnshire
PE12 9UX

Whartons Nurseries (Harleston) Ltd
Station Road, Harleston, Norfolk
IP20 9EY

Wheatcroft Ltd
Edwalton, Nottinghamshire
NG12 4DE

Trevor White Old-Fashioned Roses
'Chelt Hurst', 10 Sewell Road,
Norwich, Norfolk NR3 4BP
Mail order only

Wisbech Plant Co. Ltd
Walton Road, Wisbech,
Cambridgeshire PE13 3EF

Wyevale Nurseries Ltd
Kings Acre, Hereford & Worcester
HR4 7AY

Saintpaulia
African Violent Centre
Terrington St Clement, King's Lynn,
Norfolk PE34 4PL

Salvia
Craigieburn Classic Plants
Craigieburn House, by Moffat,
Dumfriesshire DG10 9LF

Saxifraga
Waterperry Gardens Ltd
Waterperry, Nr Wheatley, Oxfordshire
OX9 1JZ
No mail order

Sedum
Sedum Specialist
55 Beverley Drive, Choppington,
Northumberland NE62 5YA

Sempervivum
Mary & Peter Mitchell
11 Wingle Tye Road, Burgess Hill,
West Sussex RH15 9HR

Alan C Smith
127 Leaves Green Road, Keston, Kent
BR2 6DG

H & J Wills
2 St Brannocks Park Road, Ilfracombe,
Devon EX34 8HU
Mail order only

Streptocarpus
Efenechtyd Nurseries
Llanelidan, Ruthin, Clwyd LL15 2LG

Succulents – *see* **Cacti**

Thymus
Hexham Herbs
Chesters Walled Garden, Chollerford,
Hexham, Northumberland NE46 4BQ

Tillandsia
The Plant Place
63/67 Camberwell Road, London
SE5 8TR

Plantcraft
(Office) 35 Rutland Way, Orpington,
Kent BR5 4DY

Vesutor Ltd
The Bromeliad Nursery, Marringdean
Road, Billinghurst, West Sussex
RH14 9EH

Topiary
Clifton Nurseries Limited
Clifton Villas, Warwick Avenue,
London W9 2PH

Tropaeolum
Plantworld
Burnham Road, South Woodham
Ferrers, Chelmsford, Essex CM3 5QP

Tulips
Brian Duncan
Novelty & Exhibition Daffodils, 15
Ballynahatty Road, Omagh, Co.
Tyrone, Northern Ireland BT78 1PN

Walter Blom & Son Ltd
Coombelands Nurseries, Leavesdon,
Watford, Hertfordshire WD2 7BH

Vines
Cranmore Vine Nursery
Yarmouth, Isle of Wight PO41 0XS

Greenland Nurseries
11 Long Lane, Clayton West,
Huddersfield, Yorkshire HD8 9PR
Mail order only

St Annes Vineyard
Wain House, Oxenhall, Newent,
Gloucestershire GL18 1RW

Yearlstone Vineyard
Chilverton, Coldridge, Crediton,
Devon EX17 6BH

Viola
Bouts Cottage Nurseries
Bouts Lane, Inkberrow,
Worcestershire WR7 4HP
Mail order only

R G M Cawthorne
Lower Daltons Nursery, Swanley
Village, Swanley, Kent BR8 7NU
Mail order only

Cottage Garden Plants Old & New
Cox Cottage, Lower Street, East
Norden, Wareham, Dorset BH20 7DL

Rodney Fuller
Coachman's Cottage, Higher Bratton
Seymour, Wincanton, Somerset
BA9 8DA
Mail order only

C W Groves & Son
West Bay Road, Bridport, Dorset
DT6 4BA

Hazeldene Nursery
Dean Street, East Farleigh, Maidstone,
Kent ME15 0PS

Elizabeth MacGregor
Ellenbank, Tongland Road,
Kirkcudbright, Dumfries & Galloway
DG6 4UU

Elizabeth Smith
Downside, Bowling Green,
Constantine, Falmouth, Cornwall
TR11 5AP

Violet
Cottage Garden Plants Old & New
Cox Cottage, Lower Street, East
Norden, Wareham, Dorset BH20 7DL

Crankan Nurseries
New Mill, Penzance, Cornwall
TR20 8UT

Hazeldene Nursery
Dean Street, East Farleigh, Maidstone,
Kent ME15 0PS

Elizabeth MacGregory
Ellenbank, Tongland Road,
Kirkudbright, Dumfries & Galloway
DG6 4UU

Elizabeth Smith
Downside, Bowling Green,
Constantine, Falmouth, Cornwall
TR11 5AP
Mail order only

Robinson's of Whaley Bridge
20 Vaughan Road, Whaley Bridge,
Stockport, Cheshire SK12 7JT
Mail order only

Wildflowers
Arne Herbs
Limeburn Nurseries, Limeburn Hill,
Chew Magna, Avon BS18 8QW

Candlesby Herbs
Cross Keys, Candlesby, Spilsby,
Lincolnshire PE23 5SF

Fold Garden
26 Fold Lane, Biddulph, Staffordshire
ST8 7SG

Hexham Herbs
Chesters Walled Garden, Chollerford,
Hexham, Northumberland NE46 4BQ

Kingsfield Conservation Nursery
Broadenham Lane, Winsham, Chard,
Somerset TA20 4JF

Landlife Wildflowers Ltd
The Old Police Station, Lark Lane,
Liverpool L17 8UU

Marle Place Plants and Gardens
Marle Place, Brenchley, Nr Tonbridge,
Kent TN12 7HS

Salley Gardens
8 Radcliffe Mount, West Bridgford,
Nottinghamshire NG2 5FY

The Wildflower Centre
Church Farm, Sisland, Loddon,
Norwich, Norfolk NR14 6EF

The Wildlife Gardening Centre
The Apple Centre, Kingston Bagpuize,
Abingdon, Oxford OX13 5AN

MISCELLANEOUS

Australasian Plants
Tim Ingram
Copton Ash, 105 Ashford Road,
Faversham, Kent ME13 8XW

China & South Korea
Mallet Court Nursery
Curry Mallet, Taunton, Somerset
TA3 6SY

New Zealand & Falkland Island Plants
County Park Nursery
Essex Gardens, Hornchurch, Essex
RM11 3BU
No mail order

South American Plants
Greenway Gardens
Churston Ferrers, Brixham, Devon
TQ5 0ES

FRUIT

Soft Fruit
Deacon's Nursery
Moor View, Godshill, Isle of Wight
PO38 3HW

Family Trees
PO Box 3, Botley, Hampshire
SO3 2EA

Greenland Nurseries
11 Long Lane, Clayton West,
Huddersfield, Yorkshire HD8 9PR
Mail order only

Ken Muir
Honeypot Farm, Rectory Road,
Weeley Heath, Essex CO16 9BJ

Shaw Rose Trees
2 Hollowgate Hill, Willoughton,
Gainsborough, Lincolnshire DN21 5SF

Citrus & Figs
Reads Nursery
Hales Hall, Loddon, Norfolk
NR14 6QW

Fruit Trees
Deacon's Nursery
Moor View, Godshill, Isle of Wight
PO38 3HW

Eden Nurseries
Rectory Lane, Old Bolingbroke,
Spilsby, Lincolnshire PE23 4EY

The Fruit Garden
Mulberry Farm, Woodnesborough,
Sandwich, Kent CT13 0PT

Highfield Nurseries
Whitminster, Gloucestershire GL2 7PL

Mail Order: Highfield Plant & Garden
Centre, Bristol Road, Whitminster,
Gloucestershire GL2 7PB

Paul Jasper (Trees & Roses)
The Lighthouse, Bridge Street,
Leominster, Hereford & Worcester
HR6 8DU
Mail order only

Keepers Nursery
446 Wateringbury Road, East Malling,
Kent ME19 6JJ

New Trees Nurseries
2 Nunnery Road, Canterbury, Kent
CT1 3LS

J Tweedie Fruit Trees
504 Denby Dale Road West, Calder
Grove, Wakefield, Yorkshire
WF4 3DB

VEGETABLES

Asparagus
Michael Bennett
Long Compton, Shipston-on-Stour,
Warwickshire CV36 5JN
Mail order only

Trevor Sore
Marward House, Stock Corner Farm,
Bury St Edmunds, Suffolk IP28 8DW

Globe Artichoke
Michael Bennett
Long Compton, Shipston-on-Stour,
Warwickshire CV36 5JN
Mail order only

Seed Specialists

Y ou'll probably be quite surprised at the number of seedsmen there actually are. The big companies like Suttons and Unwins are the people who advertise so they're known to most of us, and it's from them that we can get most of our requirements. However, if you want something more unusual there are several specialist firms who may be able to help. Do note that some, just like the specialized nurseries, make a small charge for their catalogue.

Allwoods Bros
Hassocks, West Sussex BN6 9NB
Dianthus

Ashwood Nurseries
Greenforge, Kingswinford, West
Midlands DY6 OAE
Lewisia, cyclamen, auricula

B & T World Seeds
Whitenell House, Fiddington,
Bridgwater, Somerset TA5 1JE
Ornamentals

Bakker Holland
PO Box 11, Spalding,
Lincolnshire PE12 6EL

John Barber (Hertford) Ltd
Old Cross Wharf, Hertford SG14 1RB
General list

J W Boyce
40 Fordham, Ely, Cambridgeshire
CB7 5JU
General list

S & N Brackley
117 Winslow Road, Wingrave,
Aylesbury, Buckinghamshire
HP22 4QB
Sweet peas

D T Brown & Co Ltd
Station Road, Poulton-le-Fylde,
Blackpool FY6 7HX
General list

Bullwood Nursery
54 Woodlands Road, Hockley, Essex
SS5 4PY
Lilies & rare perennials

Thomas Butcher
60 Wickham Road, Shirley, Croydon,
Surrey CR9 8AG

Carters Seeds Ltd
Himalayan Plant Association
81 Parlaunt Road, Slough, Berkshire
SL3 8BE
*Japanese, N. American & Himalayan
seeds*

John Chambers
15 Westleigh Road, Barton Seagrave,
Kettering, Northamptonshire
NN15 5AJ
Wildflowers

Chase Organics (GB) Ltd
Coombelands House, Addlestone,
Weybridge, Surrey KT15 1HY
General list – organic

Cheshire Herbs
Fourfields, Forest Road, Little
Budworth, Cheshire CW6 9ES
Herbs

Chiltern Seeds
Bortree Stile, Ulverston, Cumbria
LA12 7PB
General list

Country Gardens
69–71 Mainstreet, East Leake,
Leicestershire LE12 6PF

Cowcombe Farm Herbs
Gipsy Lane, Chalford, Stroud,
Gloucestershire GL6 8HP
Herbs & wildflowers

Craven's Nursery
Hall Barn Nurseries, Windsor End,
Beaconsfield, Buckinghamshire
HP9 2SG
*Show auriculas, primulas, pinks &
alpines*

B & D Davies
2 Wirral View, Connah's Quay,
Deeside, Clwyd CH5 4TE
Conifers

Dig and Delve Organics
Fen Road, Blo' Norton, Diss, Norfolk
IP22 2JH

Samuel Dobie & Sons Ltd
Broomhill Way, Torquay, Devon
TQ2 7QW
General list

Jack Drake
Inshriach Alpine Nursery, Aviemore,
Invernesshire PH22 1QS
Rare alpines

Emorsgate Seed
Terrington Court, Terrington St
Clement, Kings Lynn, Norfolk
PE34 4NT
Wildflowers & grasses

Field House Nurseries
Leake Road, Gotham,
Nottinghamshire NG11 0JN
Primulas & alpines

Mr Fothergill's Seeds Ltd
Gazeley Road, Kentford, Newmarket,
Suffolk CB8 7QB
General list

Future Foods
3 Tai Madog, Stablau, Llanrug,
Gwynedd LL5 3PH

Greenholm Nursery
Lampley Road, Kingston Seymour,
Clevedon, Avon BS21 6XS
Passiflora

Harrisons Delphiniums
Newbury Cottage, Play Hatch,
Reading, Berkshire RG4 9QN
Delphiniums

James Henderson & Sons
Kingholm Quay, Dumfries DG1 4SU
Scottish seed potatoes

Holden Clough Nursery
Holden, Bolton-by-Bowland,
Clitheroe, Lancashire BB7 4PF
Alpines

W W Johnson & Son Ltd
London Road, Boston, Lincolnshire
PE21 8AD
General list

King Crown Quality Seeds
Monks Farm, Pantling Lane,
Coggleshall Road, Kelvedon, Essex
CO5 9PG
General list

Landlife Wildflowers Ltd
The Old Police Station, Lark Lane,
Liverpool L17 8UU
Native herbaceous plants

Lochside Alpine Nursery
Lochside, Ulbster, Caithness, Highland
KW2 6AA
Alpines

Mackay's Garden Centre
Castlepark Road, Sandycove, Co.
Dublin, Eire
General list

S E Marshall & Co Ltd
Regal Road, Wisbech, Cambridgeshire
PE13 2RF
General List

J E Martin
4 Church Street, Market Harborough,
Leicestershire LE16 7AA
Scottish & Dutch seed potatoes

S M McArd (Seeds)
39 West Road, Pointon, Sleaford,
Lincolnshire NG34 0NA
Unusual & giant vegetables

John Morley
North Green Only, Stoven, Beccles,
Suffolk NR34 8DG
Gelanthus, allium, fritillaria

Natural Selection
1 Station Cottages, Hullavington,
Chippenham, Wiltshire SN14 6ET
Unusual British natives

Andrew Norfield Trees & Seeds
Lower Meend, St Briavels,
Gloucestershire GL15 6RW
Ornamentals & sprouted seeds

Stuart Ogg
Hopton, Fletching Street, Mayfield,
East Sussex TN20 6TL
Delphiniums

Phedar Nursery
Bunkers Hill, Romily, Stockport,
Cheshire SK6 3DS
Helleborus

Planting Ideas Ltd
Stepfields, Witham, Essex CM8 3TA
Grass seed

Plant World Botanic Gardens
Seed Dept. (PF), St Marychurch Road,
Newton Abbot, Devon TQ12 4SE
Ornamentals

A Platt
Dower House, High Duddon,
Broughton-in-Furness, Cumbria
LA20 6ET
*Rare trees & shrubs, New Zealand
species*

Potterton & Martin
The Cottage Nursery, Moortown
Road, Nettleton, Caister, Lincolnshire
LN7 6HX
Alpines & dwarf bulbs

Roger Poulett
Nurse's Cottage, North Mundham,
Chichester, Sussex PO20 6JY
Helleborus, cyclamen, corydalis,
hepatica

W Robinson & Sons Ltd
Sunny Bank, Forton, Nr Preston,
Lancashire PR3 0BN
Mammouth vegetable seed

R V Roger Ltd
The Nurseries, Pickering, North
Yorkshire YO18 7HG
Bulbs & seed potatoes

Salley Gardens
8 Radcliffe Mount, West Bridgford,
Nottinghamshire NH2 5FY
Wildflower & medicinal herbs

Seeds by Size
70 Varney Road, Hemel Hempstead,
Hertfordshire HP1 1TB
General list

Stewart's (Nottingham) Ltd
3 George Street, Nottingham
NG1 3BH
General list

Suffolk Herbs
Sawyers Farm, Little Cornard,
Sudbury, Suffolk CO10 0NY
Herbs, wildflowers

Suttons Seeds Ltd
Hele Road, Torquay, Devon
TG2 7QJ
General list

Thompson & Morgan
London Road, Ipswich, Suffolk
IP2 0BA
General list

Thuya Alpine Nursery
Glebelands, Hartpury, Gloucestershire
GL19 3BW
Alpines

Edwin Tucker & Sons
Brewery Meadow, Stonepark,
Arbuston, Devon TQ13 7DG
Seed potatoes

Unwins Seeds Ltd
Mail Order Dept. Histon,
Cambridgeshire CB4 4ZZ
General list

Van Hage Seed Specialists
Great Amwell, Ware, Hertfordshire
SG12 9RP

Wildseeds
Branas Llandderfel, Gwynedd
LL23 7RF
Wildflowers

Roy Young Seeds
23 Westland Chase, West Winch,
King's Lynn, Norfolk PE33 0QH
Cactus & succulents

Garden Equipment and Supplies

We have many enquiries from viewers of *Gardeners' World* about products we have used on the programmes. So, to provide as much information as possible, this list includes tools, equipment and sundries that have been tried and tested at Barnsdale. We do not wish to infer that products not listed here are of inferior quality, but simply that those that are have been used over the years and are considered good value.

GC = available at garden centres.

General

Apple picker and long pruner
Bridgedale, Samuel St, Leicester
LE1 1RU

Aquatic sundries
Stapeley Water Gardens Ltd, London Road, Stapeley, Nantwich, Cheshire
CW5 7LH

Boots
Hawkins lightweight walking boots – shoe shops and sports shops.

Bow saw
Sandvik – GC.

Brassica collars
Fyba – GC.

Capillary matting
ICI – GC.

Cloches
Chase glass barn cloche – Power Garden Products, 3 Daytona Drive, Allesley, Coventry CV5 9QG

Melbourne Frames, (large field frames), MWHS, PO Box 15, Crockham Hill, Edenbridge, Kent TN8 6SG
Specialised Designs Ltd. (lantern cloche), Unit D7, Taylor Industrial Estate, Risley, Warrington WA3 6BL
Mylan Products, (tunnel cloche), Squirrels Wood, Reigate Rd, Leatherhead, Surrey KT22 8QY

Cold frames
Access Frigation Ltd, Crick, Northampton NN6 7XS

Compost
ICI Coir Compost – GC.
Goldengrow Coir Compost – GC.

Compost Bins
Garrotta bin – GC.
Rotol, Original Organics Ltd, Organic House, PO Box 6, Tiverton, Devon EX16 7SL

Hotterotter, Daisy Distribution, PO Box 595, Adstock, Buckinghamshire MK18 2RE

Disinfectant
Jeyes Fluid – GC.

Floating cloche, (spun polypropylene)
Agryl P17 – Agralan
The Old Brickyard, Ashton Keynes, Swindon, Wiltshire SN6 6QR

Fruit cage and fruit arch
Agriframes, Charlwoods Rd, East Grinstead, West Sussex RH19 2HG

Grit, Horticultural
Croxden Horticultural Products – GC.

Hormone rooting liquid
PBI Roota – GC.

Lawn fertilizer distributor
Scotts – GC.

Lawn rake (hand)
Spear and Jackson – GC.

Lawn raker (electric)
Black and Decker – GC.

Lawn Sweeper
Ginge – GC.

Lighting
Hozelock-ASL – GC.

Liquid fertilizer
Fisons Liquinure (general), Fisons Tomorite, Phostrogen (high potash) – GC

Log saw
Sandvik – GC.

Loppers
Bridgedale, Samuel St, Leicester LE1 1RU

Knife (pocket)
Victorinox – GC.

Modules (for sowing in greenhouse)
PG Horticulture, Street Farm, Thornham Magna, Eye, Suffolk IP23 8HB.
AP Propapacks – GC.

Mowers
Atco. Honda. Black and Decker. Qualcast. Alko. – GC. or garden machinery specialists.

Mulch sheet
Nortene – GC.

Netting
Nortene – GC.
Netlon – GC.

pH meter
Sudbury – GC.

Plant supports
Link Stakes, Upper Boddington, Daventry, Northamptonshire NN11 6DH
Power Garden Products, 3 Daytona Drive, Allesley, Coventry CV5 9QG

Plastic pots
Ward – GC.

Pot feet, (for raising terracotta pots)
The Terracotta Factory Shop, 35 City Rd, Newcastle-on-Tyne NE1 2AF

Propagators
Ward – GC.

Propagating blanket
Prylorn Ltd, Elmhurst Yard, High St, Chatteris, Cambridgeshire PE16 6NP

Pruning saw
Bridgedale, Samuel St, Leicester LE1 1RU

Seed trays
Ward – GC.

Secateurs
Felco – Bridgedale, Samuel St,
Leicester LE1 1RU

Shears
Wilkinson Sword – GC.

Sheep shears
Burgon and Ball, La Plata Works,
Holme Lane, Sheffield S6 4JY

Shredders
Alko – Garden machinery stockists.
Kemp – Globe Garden Services, 163A,
Warwick Rd, Solihull, West Midlands
B92 7AR

Soil warming cable
Jemp Engineering Ltd, Canal Estate,
Station Rd, Langley, Berkshire
SL3 6EG

Soil test kits
Sudbury – GC.

Sprayers
Hozelock-ASL – GC.

Strawberry mats
Fyba Products – GC.

Terracotta pots etc
Whichford Pottery, Whichford,
Shipston-on-Stour, Warwickshire
CV36 5PG

**Tools, (spades, forks, rakes, hoes,
trowels, shears, etc)**
Wilkinson Sword, Bulldog, Spear and
Jackson, Jenks and Cattell – GC.

Tree ties
Rainbow – GC.

Twine
Rainbow – GC.

Vine eyes
Rainbow – GC.

Watering cans
Haws Watering Cans, 120 Beakes Rd,
Smetwick, Warley, West Midlands
B67 5AB

Watering equipment
Hozelock-ASL – GC.
Gardena – GC.

**Waterproof tape, (for repairing glass
and clear polythene)**
Sellotape – GC.

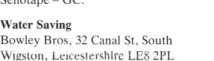

Water Saving
Bowley Bros, 32 Canal St, South
Wigston, Leicestershire LE8 2PL

Wheelbarrows
Hammerlin – GC, Builders Merchants.

Windbreak plastic
Netlon – GC.

Wood preservative
Cuprinol – GC. Builders merchants
Sadolin – Builders merchants.
PBI Woody – GC.

Wormery
Original Organics, Organic House, PO
Box 6, Tiverton, Devon EX16 7SL

Organic

Organic gardeners sometimes experience problems getting hold of the
special materials and products they
need. Most can be obtained through the
Henry Doubleday Research Association, Ryton Gardens, Coventry or
Chase Organics, Addlestone, Surrey.
The following companies can also
supply direct. (See also 'Composts and
Soil Conditioners' on p. 123.)

Biological control predators
HDRA, Ryton Gardens, Coventry,
West Midlands CV8 3LG
English Woodlands, Burrow Nursery,
Herrings Lane, Cross-in-Hand,
Heathfield, East Sussex TN21 0UG

Compost containers
see p. 97.

Environmesh insect-proof netting
Agralan, The Old Brickyard, Ashton
Keynes, Swindon, Wiltshire SN6 6QR

Fertilizers
Chase Organics (GB) Ltd, Addlestone,
Surrey KT15 1HY
Humber Fertilisers, PO Box 27,
Stoneferry, Hull HU8 8DQ
Fisons Origins Range. GC.
Greenvale Farm Ltd, Wonastow Rd,
Monmouth NP5 3XX
Maxicrop, GC.
Super-natural Ltd, Bore Place Farm,
Chiddingstone, Edenbridge, Kent
TN8 7AR

Horticultural Fleece
Agralan, The Old Brickyard, Ashton
Keynes, Swindon, Wiltshire SN6 6QR
Nortene – GC.

Grease for grease-banding
Agralan, The Old Brickyard, Ashton
Keynes, Swindon, Wiltshire SN6 6QR
Corrys grease, Synchemical – GC.

Grease bands
Boltac. PBI – GC.

Green Manure Seeds
E W King and Co Ltd, Monks Farm,
Pantlings Lane, Coggeshall Rd,
Kelvedon, Colchester, Essex CO5 9PG

Humming Line
Buzzline, Agralan, The Old Brickyard,
Ashton Keynes, Swindon, Wiltshire
SN6 6QR

Mulching sheet
(Black polythene) Nortene. GC.
(Woven) Small Lots, Higham Rd,
Burton Latimer, Northamptonshire
NN15 5PU

Papronet insect-proof plastic
Direct Wire Ties, Wyke Works,
Heddon Rd, Hull NU9 5NL

**Pheremone traps for codling moth and
plum sawfly**
Agralan, The Old Brickyard, Ashton
Keynes, Swindon, Wiltshire SN6 6QR

Yellow sticky traps for whitefly
Agralan, The Old Brickyard, Ashton
Keynes, Swindon, Wiltshire SN6 6QR

Garden Chemicals

At Barnsdale I garden completely organically without the use of man-made chemicals at all. The price I pay is a little more time controlling some pests physically, though most is done by my natural allies. I also suffer an occasional spell of nail-biting when my roses show the first signs of greenfly and I lose faith. It doesn't last long and nor do the greenfly, and the rewards are great with my garden becoming a haven for wildlife. I also enjoy the comforting knowledge that I'm not harming anything – including me.

However, you may well wish to continue to use chemicals so a list is included here. Above all, please follow to the letter the guidelines for use on the back of the bottle. The list is drawn directly from the leaflet issued by the British Agrochemicals Association – 'Garden Chemicals. A guide to their safe and effective use.' You'll find the address of the Association on p. 115.

Garden chemicals come and go. New ones appear from time to time and older ones are often withdrawn for safety reasons. This list was up to date at the time of going to press but may change during the year.

HERBICIDES AND MOSSKILLERS

No.	Trade Name	Supplier	Chemical Constituent	Harvest Interval (Days)
1	Atlacide Extra Dusting Powder	Chipman	Sodium chlorate and atrazine	00
2	Bio Lawn Weedkiller	PBI	2,4-D and dicamba	00
3	Bio Moss Killer	PBI	Dichlorophen	00
4	Bio Weed Pencil	PBI	MCPA, mecoprop and dicamba	00
5	Boots Kill-A-Weed	Boots	2,4-D, dichlorprop and mecoprop	00

No.	Trade Name	Supplier	Chemical Constituent	Harvest Interval (Days)
6	Boots Lawn Weedkiller	Boots	2,4-D. dichlorprop and mecoprop	00
7	Boots Long-Lasting Weedkiller	Boots	Amitrole and atrazine	00
8	Boots Nettle and Bramble Weedkiller	Boots	MCPA, dichlorprop and dicamba	00
9	Casoron G4	Vitax	Dichlobenil	00
10	Clean-Up	ICI	Tar acids	00
11	Couch and Grass Killer	Vitax	Dalapon	00
12	Fisons Lawn Spot Weeder	Fisons	2,4-D and dicamba	00
13	Fisons Path Weedkiller	Fisons	Amitrole, MCPA and simazine	00
14	Fisons Turf Weeds Killer	Fisons	MCPA and dicamba	00
15	Greenscape Weedkiller	Monsanto	Glyphosate	00
16	Greenscape Weedkiller Ready-to-Use	Monsanto	Glyphosate	00
17	Green Up Lawn Spot Weedkiller	Vitax	2,4-D and mecoprop	00
18	Green Up Mossfree	Vitax	Ferrous sulphate heptahydrate	00
19	Green Up Weedfree Weedkiller	Vitax	2,4-D and dicamba	00
20	Green Up Weedfree Spot Weedkiller for Lawns	Vitax	2,4-D and dicamba	00
21	Groundclear	May & Baker	Dicamba, MCPA and dichlorprop	00
22	Hytrol	Agrichem	Amitrole, 2,4-D diuron and simazine	00
23	ICI Sodium Chlorate	ICI	Sodium chlorate	00
24	Lawn Spot Weed Granules	May & Baker	2,4-D and mecoprop	00
25	Lawn Weed Gun	ICI	2,4-D and dicamba	00

No.	Trade Name	Supplier	Chemical Constituent	Harvest Interval (Days)
26	Moss Gun	ICI	Dichlorophen	00
27	Murphy Mortegg	Fisons	Tar oil	00
28	Murphy Path Weedkiller	Fisons	Amitrole and atrazine	00
29	Murphy Problem Weeds Killer	Fisons	Amitrole and MCPA	00
30	Murphy Sodium Chlorate	Fisons	Sodium chlorate	00
31	Murphy Super Moss Killer and Lawn Fungicide Ready to Use Spray	Fisons	Dichlorophen	00
32	Murphy Tumblemoss	Fisons	Chloroxuron, ferric sulphate and urea	00
33	Murphy Tumbleweed	Fisons	Glyphosate	00
34	Murphy Tumbleweed Gel	Fisons	Glyphosate	00
35	Murphy Tumbleweed Ready-to-Use	Fisons	Glyphosate	00
36	New Formula SBK Brushwood Killer	Vitax	2,4-D, mecroprop and dicamba	00
37	Path and Drive Weedkiller	May & Baker	Amitrole, ammonium, thiocyanate and simazine	00
38	Pathclear	ICI	Paraquat, diquat, simazine and aminotriazole	00
39	Supertox Lawn Weed Killer	May & Baker	2,4-D and mecroprop	00
40	Supertox Spot Weeder	May & Baker	2,4-D and mecroprop	00
41	Super Weedex	Fisons	Amitrole and simazine	00
42	Total Weedkiller Granules	May & Baker	Simazine and diuron	00
43	Verdone 2	ICI	Mecroprop and 2,4-D	00
44	Weedex	Fisons	Simazine	00

No.	Trade Name	Supplier	Chemical Constituent	Harvest Interval (Days)
45	Weed Out Couchgrass Killer	May & Baker	Alloxydim-sodium	00
46	Weedol	ICI	Paraquat and diquat	00
47	Autumn Extra	Fisons	Ferrous sulphate	00
48	Boots Lawn Mosskiller and Fertiliser	Boots	Ferrous sulphate	00
49	Boots Lawn Weed and Feed Peat Based granules	Boots	Mecoprop and 2,4-D	00
50	Boots Lawn Weed and Feed Soluble Powder	Boots	Dichlorprop and MCPA	00
51	Boots Spring and Autumn Lawn Treatment	Boots	Dichlorophen	00
52	Boots Total Lawn Treatment	Boots	Dichlorophen, mecoprop dichlorprop, 2,4-D, dicamba and benazolin	00
53	Fisons Evergreen 90	Fisons	MCPA and mecoprop	00
54	Fisons Evergreen Extra	Fisons	MCPA, mecoprop and ferrous sulphate	00
55	Fisons Lawncare Liquid Lawn Fertilizer and Weedkiller	Fisons	MCPA, mecoprop and dicamba	00
56	Fisons Lawn Seed	Fisons	Ferrous sulphate	00
57	Fisons Mosskill Extra	Fisons	Ferrous sulphate	00
58	Green Up Feed & Weed, plus Mosskiller	Vitax	2,4-D, mecoprop and ferous sulphate	00
59	Green Up Lawn Feed & Weed	Vitax	2,4-D and dicamba	00
60	ICI Mosskiller for Lawns	ICI	Ferrous suphate and fertilizers	00
61	Lawn Feed and Weed Granules	May & Baker	2,4-D and mecoprop plus fertilizers	00

No.	Trade Name	Supplier	Chemical Constituent	Harvest Interval (Days)
62	Lawnsman Liquid Weed and Feed	ICI	Dicamba, dichlorprop MCPA and fertilizer	00
63	Lawnsman Mosskiller	ICI	Dichlorophen, chloroxuron and ferrous sulphate	00
64	Lawnsman Weed and Feed	ICI	2,4-D and dicamba	00
65	Lawnsman Spot Weed Granules	May & Baker	Weedkiller and fertilizer	00
66	Murphy Lawn Weedkiller and Lawn Tonic	Fisons	2,4-D and dichlorprop plus urea	00
67	Supergreen and Weed	May & Baker	2,4-D, mecoprop and NPK fertilizer	00
68	Supergreen Feed, Weed and Mosskiller	May & Baker	2,4-D, mecoprop, ferrous sulphate and NPK fertilizer	00
69	Toplawn	PBI	2,4-D and dicamba	00
70	Triple Action Grasshopper (with refill)	ICI	2,4-D, dicamba, ferrous sulphate and fertilizer	00
71	Velvas	PBI	Ferrous sulphate	00
72	Velvetone Lawn Food and Weedkiller	Fisons	2,4-D and dicamba	00

INSECTICIDES AND MITE CONTROL

No.	Trade Name	Supplier	Chemical Constituent	Harvest Interval (Days)
73	Anti-Ant Duster	PBI	Pyrethrum	00
74	Ant Gun	ICI	Diazinon and pyrethrins	00
75	Bio Crop Saver	PBI	Permethrin and malathion	1
76	Bio Flydown	PBI	Permethrin	00
77	Bio Friendly Anti-Ant Duster	PBI	Pyrethrum	00

No.	Trade Name	Supplier	Chemical Constituent	Harvest Interval (Days)
78	Bio Friendly Insect Spray	PBI	Derris and quassia	00
79	Bio Friendly Pest Pistol	PBI	Horticultural soaps	00
80	Bio Long-last	PBI	Dimthoate and permethrin	7
81	Bio Multirose	PBI	Permethrin, triforine, dinocap sulphur and fertilizer	00
82	Bio Sprayday	PBI	Permethrin and piperonyl butoxide	00
83	Boots Ant Killer	Boots	Carbaryl and borax	00
84	Boots Caterpillar and Whitefly Killer	Boots	Permethrin	1
85	Boots Garden Insect Powder with Derris	Boots	Carbaryl and rotenone	7
86	Boots Greenfly and Blackfly Killer	Boots	Dimthoate	7
87	Boots Kill-A-Bug	Boots	Permethrin and boiallethrin	00
88	Bromophos	PBI	Bromophos	7
89	Bug Gun for Fruit and Vegetables	ICI	Natural pyrethrum	00
90	Bug Gun for Roses and Flowers	ICI	Natural pyrethrum	00
91	Clean-up	ICI	Tar acids	00
92	Derris Dust	Vitax	Rotenone	1
93	Fenitrothion	PBI	Fenitrothion	14 (7 for raspberries)
94	Fisons Insect Spray for Houseplants	Fisons	Permethrin	00
95	Fisons Nature's Answer to Insect Pests on Flowers, Fruit and Vegetables	Fisons	Pyrethrum	00

No.	Trade Name	Supplier	Chemical Constituent	Harvest Interval (Days)
96	Fumite General Purpose Greenhouse Insecticide Smokes	ICI	Pirimiphos-methyl	00
97	Fumite Whitefly Greenhouse Insecticide Smokes	ICI	Permethrin	00
98	Hexyl	PBI	Gamma-HCH, retenone thiram	14
99	House Plant Pest Killer	Vitax	Pyrethrum and resmethrin	00
100	ICI Ant Killer Dust	ICI	Pirimiphos-methyl	00
101	ICI Derris Dust	ICI	Rotenone	1
102	Keriguards	ICI	Dimethoate plus fertilizer	00
103	Kerispray	ICI	Pirimiphos-methyl and synergized pyrethrins	00
104	Kybosh	PBI	Permethrin and synergized pyrethrins	00
105	Liquid Derris	PBI	Rotenone	1
106	Malathion Greenfly Killer	PBI	Malathion	1
107	Murphy Combined Seed Dressing	Fisons	Captan and gamma HCH	00
108	Murphy Derris Dust	Fisons	Rotenone	1
109	Murphy Gamma-BHC Dust	Fisons	Gamma-HCH	14
110	Murphy Kil-Ant	Fisons	Phoxim	00
111	Murphy Lawn Pest Killer	Fisons	Carbaryl	00
112	Murphy Liquid Malathion	Fisons	Malathion	4
113	Murphy Malathion Dust	Fisons	Malathion	4
114	Murphy Mortegg	Fisons	Tar oil	00

No.	Trade Name	Supplier	Chemical Constituent	Harvest Interval (Days)
115	Murphy Permethrin Whitefly Smoke (Cone)	Fisons	Permethrin	00
116	Murphy Pest and Disease Smoke (Cone)	Fisons	Gamma-HCH and tecnazene	2
117	Murphy Soil Pests Killer	Fisons	Phoxim	00
118	Murphy Systemic Action Insecticide	Fisons	Heptenophos and permethrin	1
119	Murphy Tumblebug	Fisons	Permethrin and heptenophos	1
120	Murphy Zap Cap Combined Insecticide and Fungicide	Fisons	Permethrin (P) and fenarimol (F)	PO F14 Combined 14
121	Murphy Zap Cap General Insecticide	Fisons	Permethrin	00
122	Nippon Ant and Crawling Insect Killer	Vitax	Permethrin and tetramethrin	00
123	Nippon Ant Killer Liquid	Vitax	Borax	00
124	Nippon Ant Killer Powder	Vitax	Permethrin	00
125	Nippon Fly Killer Spray	Vitax	Tetramethrin and permethrin	00
126	Nippon Ready for Use Ant and Crawling Insect Spray	Vitax	Permethrin	00
127	Picket	ICI	Permethrin	00
128	Py Garden Insecticide	Vitax	Pyrethrum and piperonyl butoxide	1
129	Py Powder	Vitax	Pyrethrum and piperonyl butoxide	1
130	Pyrethrum Garden Insect Killer	Vitax	Pyrethrum and piperonyl butoxide	1
131	Py Spray Insect Killer	Vitax	Pyrethrum and piperonyl butoxide	1

No.	Trade Name	Supplier	Chemical Constituent	Harvest Interval (Days)
132	Rapid Aerosol	ICI	Pirimicarb	3 (14 days lettuce under glass)
133	Rapid Greenfly	ICI	Pirimicarb	3 (14 days lettuce under glass)
134	Roseclear	ICI	Bupirimate, triforine and pirimicarb	00
135	Sybol	ICI	Pirimiphos-methyl	7
136	Sybol Aerosol	ICI	Pirimiphos-methyl and synergized pyrethrins	7
137	Sybol Dust	ICI	Pirimiphos-methyl	7
138	Waspend	ICI	Pirimiphos-methyl and synergized pyrethrins	00

INSECTICIDES/FERTILIZER MIXTURE

No.	Trade Name	Supplier	Chemical Constituent	Harvest Interval (Days)
139	Autumn Toplawn	PBI	Carbaryl and fertilizer	00

FUNGICIDES

No.	Trade Name	Supplier	Chemical Constituent	Harvest Interval (Days)
140	Benlate + Activex 2	ICI	Benomyl	00
141	Bio Moss Killer	PBI	Dichlorophen	00
142	Bio Multirose	PBI	Triforine, dinocap sulphur, permethrin and fertilizer	00
143	Boots Garden Fungicide	Boots	Carbendazim	1 (14 lettuce)
144	Bordeaux Mixture	Vitax	Copper sulphate	00
145	Cheshunt Compound	PBI	Copper sulphate and ammonium	00

No.	Trade Name	Supplier	Chemical Constituent	Harvest Interval (Days)
146	Dithane 945	PBI	Mancozeb	7 (21 for lettuce)
147	Green and Yellow Sulphur	Vitax	Sulphur	00
148	Hexyl	PBI	Gamma-HCH, rotenone and thiram	14
149	Liquid Club Root Control	May & Baker	Thiophanate-methyl	00
150	Murphy Combined Seed Dressing	Fisons	Captan and Gamma-HCH	00
151	Murphy Pest and Disease Smoke	Fisons	Tecnazene and gamma-HCH	2
152	Murphy Systemic Action Fungicide	Fisons	Carbendazim	00
153	Murphy Traditional Copper Fungicide	Fisons	Copper oxychloride	00
154	Murphy Tumbleblite	Fisons	Propiconazole	00
155	Murphy Zap Cap Combined Insecticide and Fungicide	Fisons	Permethrin (P) and Fenarimol (F)	P0 F14 Combined 14
156	Murphy Zap Cap Systemic Fungicide	Fisons	Carbendazim	0 (14 lettuce)
157	Nimrod-T	ICI	Bupirimate and triforine	Apples 7 (Black-currant/goose-berry 14)
158	Roseclear	ICI	Bupirimate, triforine and pirimicarb	00
159	Supercarb	PBI	Carbendazim and an activator	0 (14 lettuce)
160	Systemic Fungicide Liquid	May & Baker	Thiophanate-methyl	00
161	Systhane	PBI	Myclobutanil	00

No.	Trade Name	Supplier	Chemical Constituent	Harvest Interval (Days)

SLUG, SNAIL AND WORM CONTROLS AND OTHER PRODUCTS

No.	Trade Name	Supplier	Chemical Constituent	Harvest Interval (Days)
162	Arbrex Pruning Compound	PBI	Bitumen	00
163	Autumn and Winter Toplawn	PBI	Carbaryl and fertilizer	00
164	Bio Friendly Pest and Disease Duster	PBI	Derris and sulphur	00
165	Bio Roota	PBI	1-naphthylacetic acid and dichlorophen	00
166	Boltac Greasebands	PBI		00
167	Boots Hormone Rooting Powder	Boots	1-naphthylacetic acid, 4-(indol-3-yl) butyric acid and thiram	00
168	Boots Slug Destroyer Mini-Pellets	Boots	Metaldehyde	00
169	Clean-up	ICI	Tar acid	00
170	Corry's Fruit Tree Grease	Vitax		00
171	Cutlass	ICI	Dikegulac	00
172	ICI Mini Slug Pellets	ICI	Metaldehyde	00
173	Medo	Vitax	Cresylic acid	00
174	Mosgo	Agrichem	Sodium pentachlorophenoxide	00
175	Mouser	ICI	Brodifacoum	00
176	Murphy Hormone Rooting Powder	Fisons	1-naphthylacetic acid and captan	00
177	Murphy Lawn Pest Killer	Fisons	Carbaryl	00
178	Murphy Mole Smoke	Fisons	Sulphur	00
179	Murphy Mortegg	Fisons	Tar oil	00

No.	Trade Name	Supplier	Chemical Constituent	Harvest Interval (Days)
180	Murphy Slugit Liquid	Fisons	Metaldehyde	10
181	Murphy Slugits	Fisons	Metaldehyde	00
182	Murphy Slugtape	Fisons	Metaldehyde	00
183	Pepper Dust	PBI	Pepper Powder	00
184	Pepper Dust	Vitax	Pepper Powder	00
185	Racumin Mouse Bait	PBI	Coumatetralyl	00
186	Racumin Rat Bait	PBI	Coumatetralyl	00
187	Ratak	ICI	Difenacoum	00
188	Rooting Powder	Vitax	Captan and 1-naphthylacetic acid	00
189	Scent Off Buds	Vitax	Naphthalene and scented oils	00
190	Scent Off Pellets	Vitax	Naphthalene and volatile oils	00
191	Slug Gard	PBI	Methiocarb	00
192	Slug Mini Pellets	PBI	Metaldehyde	00
193	Stay-Off	Vitax	Aluminium ammonium sulphate	00
194	Strike	May & Baker	1-naphthylacetic acid	00
195	Tomato Setting Spray	Vitax	2-Naphthyloxy acid	00

Herbicides and mosskillers to use

Bramble	8, 29
Clover	43
Couch grass	11, 45
Lawn weeds	2, 4, 5, 6, 12, 14, 17, 19, 20, 24, 25, 30, 39, 40, 43, 48
Moss	3, 10, 18, 26, 27, 31, 32, 169, 174, 179
Tree stumps/Woody weeds	21, 36
Weeds (general)	1, 4, 5, 7, 9, 13, 15, 16, 22, 23, 28, 30, 33, 34, 35, 37, 38, 41, 42, 44, 46

Herbicides/fertilizer mixtures to use

Lawn weeds	48, 49, 50, 51, 52, 53, 55, 57, 58, 59, 61, 62, 63, 64, 65, 66, 67, 68, 69, 70, 71, 72
Moss	47, 54, 56, 58, 60, 114, 174, 179
Weeds (general)	54

Products for insect control to use

Ants	73, 74, 77, 83, 100, 104, 110, 111, 112, 123, 124, 126, 129, 138
Aphids	92, 99, 106, 128, 129
Beetles	104, 108
Blackfly	78, 79, 82, 86, 93, 94, 105, 106, 118, 121, 132, 133, 134, 158, 164
Capsids	93
Caterpillars	78, 82, 84, 85, 92, 93, 105, 108, 115, 121, 127, 128, 129, 164, 166
Chafers	111
Cockroaches	74, 108, 110, 122, 124, 126, 128
Codling Moth	93
Crawling Insects	74, 104, 110, 122, 124, 126, 130, 138
Earwigs	100, 110
Flea Beetle	92, 129
Flies	74, 125, 138
Glasshouse Pests	90, 91, 96, 97, 115, 116, 132, 135, 136, 137
Greenfly	75, 76, 78, 79, 82, 86, 93, 94, 99, 105, 106, 108, 112, 113, 118, 121, 132, 133, 134, 158, 164
Insects (general)	80, 87, 89, 95, 98, 101, 103, 119, 130, 131, 136, 137
Insects (on veg)	75, 87, 89
Leaf Minor	82, 106
Leatherjackets	85, 109, 111, 139, 163, 177, 191
Mealybugs	94, 106, 112
Millepedes	190
Pea Maggot	84
Raspberry Beetle	93, 105
Red Spider Mite	79, 92, 94, 99, 103, 105, 106, 112, 136, 137
Rootfly Beetles	109
Rose Pests	81, 90, 114
Sawfly	93, 105
c/o Seeds and Seedlings	107, 150
Silverfish	74

Soft Scale	79, 94, 106, 112
Soil Pests	88, 117
Thrips	78, 82, 92, 94, 105, 106, 113, 115, 121
Wasps	74, 100, 104, 124, 125, 138
Whitefly	75, 76, 79, 82, 84, 94, 97, 99, 103, 106, 112, 113, 115, 118, 121, 127, 128, 136, 137
Wire Worms	85, 109
Woodlice	74, 100, 110, 191

Products for disease control to use

Apple Scab	146, 156
Blackspot	120, 134, 154, 155, 156, 157, 158, 161
Botrytis	156
Canker	144, 173
Club Root (on brassicas)	149
General (Garden & Greenhouse)	140, 143
Lawn Diseases	141
Leaf Mould	144, 146
Leaf Spot	144, 146, 155, 156, 157
Mildew	134, 146, 147, 154, 155, 156, 157, 158, 161, 164
Peach Leaf Curl	144, 146, 153
Pear Scab	146, 156
Potato Blight	144, 146, 153
Powdery Mildew	154, 155, 156, 157
Rose Pests	142
Rose Rust	146, 158, 161
Rots	147
Rusts	144, 146, 154, 161
c/o Seeds & Seedlings	145, 150, 153
Tomato Blight	144

Slugs, snail, worm and other animal controls to use

Birds	193
Cats and Dogs	183, 184, 188, 189, 190, 193
Mice	175, 178, 184, 185, 186, 187
Moles	178
Rats	178, 186, 187
Slugs	168, 172, 179, 180, 181, 182, 191, 192
Snails	168, 172, 179, 180, 181, 182, 191, 192
Worms	163, 177

Addresses

British Agrochemical Association Ltd
4 Lincoln Court, Lincoln Road,
Peterborough PE1 2RP

BAA members supplying chemicals

Agrichem International Ltd
Industrial Estate, Station Road,
Whittlesey, Cambridgeshire PE7 2EY
Tel: 0733 204019 *Fax*: 0733 204162

Atlas Interlates Ltd
Glasshouse Farm, PO Box 38, Low
Moor, Bradford, West Yorkshire
BD12 0JZ
Tel: 0274 671267 *Fax*: 0274 691482

Boots Company plc
Leisure Business Centre, The
Frontage, Queen Street, Nottingham
NG2 3AA
Tel: 0602 866671 *Fax*: 0602 860695
Telex: 378431

Chipman Ltd
Portland Buildings, Portland Street,
Staple Hill, Bristol, Avon BS16 4PS
Tel: 0272 575828 *Fax*: 0272 563461

Fisons plc
Horticulture Division, Paper Mill
Lane, Bramford, Ipswich, Suffolk
IP8 4BZ
Tel: 0473 830492 *Fax*: 0473 830046
Telex: 98168

ICI Garden Products
Woolmead House, Woolmead Walk,
Farnham, Surrey GU9 7UB
Tel: 0252 733919 *Fax*: 0252 736222
Telex: 858347

May & Baker Garden Care
Fyfield Road, Ongar, Essex
CM5 0HW
Tel: 0277 362127 *Fax*: 0277 264087
Telex: 28691

Monsanto Garden Care
Thames Tower, Burleys Way,
Leicester LE1 3TP
Tel: 0533 620864 *Fax*: 0533 530320
Telex: 34658

Pan Britannica Industries
Britannica House, Waltham Cross,
Hertfordshire EN8 7DY
Tel: 0992 23691 *Fax*: 0992 26452
Telex: 23957

Vitax Ltd
Owen Street, Coalville, Leicester
LE6 2DE
Tel: 0530 510060 *Fax*: 0530 510299

Pest and disease control permitted by the Soil Association

Mechanical controls using traps,
    barriers and sound
Pheromones
Herbal sprays, homeopathic and
    biodynamic preparations
Waterglass (sodium silicate)
Bicarbonate of soda
Soft soap
Steam sterilization
Biological control with naturally
    occuring organisms
Conventionally grown seed –
    recleaned only
Symbol approved products.

Nutrients

All plants require nutrients in the form of chemical salts which they absorb in solution. There are three major elements – nitrogen, phosphorous and potassium which are needed in relatively large amounts. The so-called 'trace elements' are needed in much smaller quantities, but are none the less essential.

The amount of each major element contained in compound fertilizers is marked on the bag, using the chemical symbols N for nitrogen, P for phosphorous and K for potassium. Often there are only figures showing the percentage of each element but always in that order. So, a bag of fertilizer marked '7.5.6.' would contain 7% nitrogen, 5% phosphorous and 6% potassium.

Trace elements are not marked on the bag and indeed, many chemical fertilizers don't contain them. However, soils that are rich in organic matter in the form of regularly applied compost or manure are unlikely to be short. If deficiencies do occur they can generally be rectified by feeding with seaweed.

The Need for Feed

Major plant nutrients

NITROGEN (N)
Nitrogen controls the rate of growth, protein development and photosynthesis.
Deficiency symptoms: stunted growth, pale leaves with yellow or red tints, fruit smaller and highly coloured.
Treatment: top dress with nitrogenous fertilizer. Also add compost or manure when digging.

PHOSPHOROUS (P)
Phosphorous in phosphates encourages healthy root growth as well as the ripening of fruit.
Deficiency symptoms: poor growth (especially roots), blue or purple-tinted leaves, low fruit yields.
Treatment: top dress with superphosphate or, alternatively, balanced fertilizer.

POTASSIUM (K)
Potassium in the form of potash aids the usefulness of nitrogen, enhances the colour and quality of fruit and flowers, and sustains general good health overall.

Deficiency symptoms: poor quality produce, low yields, leaf mottling, or marginal scorching.
Treatment: dress with sulphate of potash or balanced fertilizer before sowing.

CALCIUM (Ca)
Calcium adjusts soil acidity/alkalinity and helps the assimilation of nitrogen and the formation of plant cell walls.
Deficiency symptoms: growing tips scorched or die back, fruit disorders (bitter pit in apples, tomato blossom end rot).
Treatment: lime acid soils, spray affected fruit with calcium nitrate solution and avoid irregular watering.

MAGNESIUM (Mg)
Magnesium aids chlorophyll production and seed germination.
Deficiency symptoms: dead or discoloured patches between leaf veins, orange, brown or red tints on foliage, fall of young leaves.
Treatment: lime with magnesium limestone (dolomite) if calcium also deficient; use 1oz Epsom salts (magnesium sulphate) in 1 gal water/sq yd.

Minor plant nutrients

These plant nutrients, often called trace elements, are only needed in very small quantities, but are vital for healthy growth.

IRON (Fe)
Iron helps the formation of chlorophyll.
Deficiency symptoms: complete leaves pale or whitish/yellow (chlorosis), especially in very alkaline soils.
Treatment: apply sequestered iron and guard against excessive liming.

MANGANESE (Mn)
Manganese is thought to help form chlorophyll.
Deficiency symptoms: chlorosis between veins which become bright green, leaf rolling.
Treatment: avoid over-liming, spray affected plants with manganese sulphate.

BORON (B)
Boron helps the movement of nutrients within plants.
Deficiency symptoms: rough patches on fruits and leaves, brown hearts in vegetables.
Treatment: correct soil deficiency by raking in borax at 1oz/10sq yd.

MOLYBDENUM (Mo)
Molybdenum is linked to nitrogen absorption.
Deficiency symptoms: distorted leaf blades and growing tips, whiptail in cauliflowers on acid soils.
Treatment: lime acid soils before growing susceptible plants such as brassicas.

COPPER (Cu)
Copper has an uncertain nutritional role.
Deficiency symptoms: wilt and death of young leaves and shoots, often on peaty soils.
Treatment: difficult – foliar feed with complete fertilizer containing trace elements.

ZINC (Zn)
Zinc aids starch production and balanced growth.
Deficiency symptoms: leaf and shoot distortion, brown buds, usually on light soils.
Treatment: as for copper, and avoid over-liming.

Fertilizers

Fertilizers are available in several forms. Firstly there are solid, liquid and soluble fertilizers: solids are generally longer-lasting but, since they can only be taken up in solution, are somewhat slower acting. Liquids are more readily available but more quickly leached out of the soil, while soluble fertilizers come in the form of a powder which is dissolved in water to form a liquid fertilizer.

Controlled-release fertilizers are now also available to amateur gardeners and they can be extremely useful. They consist of granular feeds which are treated to allow the release of the nutrients generally as temperatures rise. So, when the roots are not growing actively in low temperatures, the fertilizer is unavailable. When soil temperatures increase, so the fertilizer becomes more available. It's possible to buy formulations which remain available for 3–4 months and others for 6–9 months, so saving much labour in hand feeding.

Fertilizers are also bought either as 'straights', delivering just one of the three main nutrients, nitrogen, phosphorous or potassium, or as 'general' fertilizers containing all three in various formulations. A high nitrogen fertilizer is used, for example, to stimulate growth while a high potassium (or potash) feed is used to encourage flowering and fruiting.

Finally, there are organic and chemical fertilizers. While plants take up minerals in the same form, regardless of whether the source is organic or chemical, there are differences.

Organic fertilizers generally do no harm to soil organisms which are needed to break down the materials and make them available to plant roots. For this reason most are also longer lasting but not so immediately available.

Chemical fertilizers tend to depress the activity of soil organisms and it's thought that they can eventually deplete the soil of them entirely. However, they are more readily available but are leached out of the soil faster.

So, organic fertilizers are used to gradually increase fertility in the soil and require the presence of organic matter to sustain the organisms that break them down. Chemical fertilizers feed the plant directly and will work in completely mineral soils or even in hydroponic systems.

Key

O = organic. C = chemical.
L = liquid. S = solid. Sol. = soluble.
SM = several manufacturers.

GC = available at garden centres.
BT&T+ Barnsdale Tried and Tested.

General Fertilizers

Acid-lovers Fertilizer
see Ericaceous Fertilizers.

African Violet Fertilizer
C S   Garden Direct, Geddings
Road, Hoddesdon, Hertfordshire
EN11 0LR

Blood, fish and bone meal
O S SM GC. BT&T

Bonsai Tree Fertilizer
C S   Garden Direct.

Cactus and Succulent Fertilizer
C S   Garden Direct.

Calcified seaweed
O S SM GC. BT&T.

Carnation Base
C S   Garden Direct.

Chempak Multipurpose Base
C S   Garden Direct.

Chempak Potting Base
C S   Garden Direct.   BT&T

Chempak Seed Base
C S   Garden Direct.   BT&T

**Chempak Soluble Plant Foods (4
formulations)**
C Sol.   Garden Direct.   BT&T.

Chicken Manure (pelletted)
O S   Fisons Origins Range.
GC. BT&T.

Chicken Manure (pelletted)
O S   Greenvale Farm, Wonastow
Road, Monmouth.   BT&T.

Coir Liquid Feed
C L ICI GC.   BT&T

Controlled Release Fertilizer
C S   Osmocote. Garden Direct.
BT&T

Controlled Release Fertilizer
C S   Fisons Unifeed GC.   BT&T.

**Controlled Release Houseplant
Fertilizer**
C S   Fisons Long Lasting Feed.
GC.

Ericaceous Base
C S   Garden Direct.

Ericaceous Fertilizer
C L   Arthur Bowers. GC.

Ericaceous Fertilizer
C Sol. ICI Miracid. GC.
BT&T.

Foliar feed
C L   PBI Fillip. GC.

Flower and Bedding Plus
C S ICI GC.

Flower and Fruit Fertilizer
C S   Garden Direct.

Flower Fertilizer
C L   Bio Flower Maker. GC.

Foliage Fertilizer
C L   Bio Leaf Maker. GC.

Growmore
C L SM GC. BT&T.

Growmore
C S SM GC. BT&T.

Green Foliage Fertilizer
C S   Garden Direct.

Houseplant Fertilizer
C L SM GC.

Humic and Fulvic Acid Booster
O L   Bio Humigro. GC.

John Innes Base
C S SM GC. BT&T.

Morgro
O S   Garden Direct.

Orchid Fertilizer
C S   Garden Direct.

Organic Garden All Purpose Fertilizer
O S   Arthur Bowers. GC.
BT&T.

Plant Food Tablets
C S   Phostrogen. GC.

Potato Fertilizer
C S   Arthur Bowers. GC. BT&T.

Rhododendron Plus
C S ICI GC. BT&T.

Rose Fertilizer
C S SM GC. BT&T.

Rose Fertilizer
C L SM GC. BT&T.

Seaweed Meal
O S   Garden Direct. BT&T.

Seaweed Extract
O L SM GC. BT&T.

Shrub and Tree Plus
C S ICI GC.

Soluble General Fertilizer
C Sol. Phostrogen. GC.
BT&T.

Variegated Foliage Fertilizer
C S   Garden Direct.

Vegetable Plus
C S ICI GC. BT&T.

Lawn Fertilizers

Autumn Lawn Food
C S SM GC.

Controlled Release Lawn Food
C S   Scotts. GC. BT&T.

Spring and Summer Lawn Food
C S SM GC. BT&T.

Spring and Summer Lawn Food
C L SM GC. BT&T.

Organic Lawn Food
O S   Fisons Origins. GC.
BT&T.

Lawn Weed and Feed

Lawn Weed and Feed
C L SM GC.

Lawn Weed and Feed
C S SM GC. BT&T.

Trace Elements

Sequestered Trace Elements
C L   Garden Direct.

Trace Element Frit
C S   Garden Direct. BT&T.

Kieserite (magnesium)
O S   Garden Direct.

Magnesium Sulphate
C S Garden Direct.

Manganese Sulphate
C S Garden Direct

Sequestered Iron
C S Murphy Sequestrine. GC.
BT&T.

Sodium Molybdate
C S Garden Direct

Straights

Aluminium Sulphate (blueing agent)
C S SM GC. BT&T.

Ammonium Nitrate
C Sol. Garden Direct.

Basic Slag
C S Garden Direct.

Bonemeal
O S SM GC. BT&T.

Borax
C Sol. Garden Direct.

Calcium Nitrate
C L Garden Direct.

Chelated Iron
C Sol. Garden Direct.

Chempak Fish Emulsion
O L Garden Direct.

Chilean Nitrate of Potash
O S Garden Direct.

Dolomite Lime
O S SM GC. BT&T.

Dried Blood
O S SM GC. BT&T.

Epsom Salts
C S Arthur Bowers. GC. BT&T.

Fish Meal
O S SM GC. BT&T.

Hoof and Horn
O S SM GC. BT&T.

Mono Ammonium Sulphate
C S Garden Direct.

Muriate of Potash
C S Garden Direct. BT&T.

Nitrate of Soda
C S SM GC.

Nitrochalk
C S Garden Direct. BT&T.

Potassium Nitrate
C S Arthur Bowers. GC.

Rock Potash
O S SM GC. BT&T.

Sulphate of Ammonia
C S SM GC. BT&T.

Sulphate of Iron
C S SM GC.

Sulphate of Potash
C S SM GC. BT&T.

Superphosphate
C S SM GC. BT&T.

Triple superphosphate
C S Garden Direct.

Organic Fertilizers permitted under Soil Association standards

Rock Phosphate
Feldspar
Magnesium Limestone (dolomite)
Calcium Sulphate (gypsum)
Ground Chalk and Limestone

Seaweed (free from non-approved
   products)
Unadulterated Seaweed and Plant-
   based Foliar sprays
Calcified Seaweed
Basic Slag
Rock Potash
Symbol approved organic
   fertilizers/liquid feeds

Wood Ash
Meat, Bone, Hoof and Horn meals
Fish meal
Unadulterated Fish Blood and Bone
   meals
Calcined Aluminium Phosphate

Fertilizers restricted under Soil Association standards

Proprietary organic fertilizers and
   liquid feeds without symbol approval
Dried blood – in spring or on
   overwintered crops
Wool Shoddy, Hop Waste
Leather Meal
Sulphate of Potash – only where
   exchangeable K levels are low and
   clay content is less than 20%
Sulphate of Potash – magnesium
Kieserite
Borax
Epsom salts

Composts and Soil Conditioners

As a result of our concern for the conservation of peat bogs and the many letters from viewers urging us to take a lead in finding alternatives, much work has been done at Barnsdale to assess various products. It has generally been accepted that there is no need to use peat as a soil conditioner and there are many good alternatives available.

Finding a suitable compost for sowing and potting in the greenhouse proved more difficult and the work is still progressing. However, there are some products which we now feel confident in recommending.

It should be pointed out that, just as gardeners needed to get used to peat after using soil based composts, new media may need different treatment. Some of our trials have been very successful and some have failed, but we don't suggest that this implies that those materials which proved less successful are worthless. More time is needed to ensure that we are using them to their best advantage, and the trials will continue. The composts listed here are those that have proved successful so far.

Soil Conditioners and Mulches

GC = Available at Garden Centres.

Arthur Bowers Mulch and Mix
GC.

Arthur Bowers Horse Manure Compost
GC.

Arthur Bowers Rose Ultra Bark

Arthur Bowers Conifer Ultra Bark

Arthur Bowers Ericaceous Ultra Bark

Arthur Bowers Composted Ultra Bark

Arthur Bowers Decorative Bark Chips
GC.

Cambark Horticultural Products (a range of bark products)
GC.

Danu Organic Soil Conditioner
Earthcare Products, Dromiskin, Dundalk, Eire. (and GC)

Fisons Composted Bark
GC.

Fisons Woodland Chipped Bark
GC.

Good Gardener All Purpose Bark
Garden Direct, Geddings Rd,
Hoddesdon, Hertfordshire EN1 0LR

Heritage Soil Enricher
Waste Refineries International, Unit 3,
The Home, Eaton, Craven Arms,
Shropshire SY9 5HU

ICI Forest Bark
GC.

ICI Forest Mulch
GC.

John McLaughlan Horticulture, (wood fibre products)
50A, Market Place, Thirsk, North
Yorkshire YO7 1LH

Lady Muck, (cow slurry soil conditioner)
Marshwood House, Whitegate, Forton,
Chard, Somerset TA20 4HL (and GC).

Melcourt Industries, (a range of bark mulches and soil conditioners)
Eight Bells House,
Tetbury,Gloucestershire GL8 8JG

Sunshine of Africa Cocoashell
Garden Direct, Geddings Rd,
Hoddesdon, Hertfordshire EN11 0LR
(and GC).

UF Soil Conditioner

UF Tree Planting and Shrub Compost

UF All Purpose Mulch

UF Decorative Mulch

UF Chip and Bark Mulch

UF Manure
UF Horticulture, Stallard Common,
Great Ellingham, Attleborough,
Norfolk NR17 1JF

Composts

Chempak Coir

Chempak Coir Compost
Garden Direct, Geddings Rd,
Hoddesdon, Hertfordshire EN11 0LR

Fisons Multipurpose Peat-free Compost
GC.

Goldengrow Multipurpose Cocofibre Compost.

Goldengrow Cocofibre Growing Bag

Goldengrow Ericaceous Cocofibre Compost
Goldengrow Ltd, Firth Rd, Lincoln
LN6 7AH

Godwins Fruit of the Earth Compost
GC.

Heritage Multipurpose Compost

Heritage Coconut Fibre
Waste Refineries International, Unit 3,
The Home, Eaton, Craven Arms,
Shropshire SY9 5HU

ICI Coir Compost
GC.

John Innes Composts
GC.

Wessex Cococompost
GC.

Using coir composts

Coir composts look like peat but have very different properties, so you'll need to get used to a slightly different technique. The following points should be considered:

1. It's water-holding capacity is very good, but the top 15mm(½in) or so tends to dry out quickly. To avoid the temptation to overwater, push your fingers down below the top of the compost to test for moisture until you get used to it.

2. Ideally, rest the pots and seed trays on capillary matting and keep that wet so that water is drawn up from the bottom.

3. Start to feed much earlier than you have done with peat composts. They often need it in the second or third week after potting. Feed with a special liquid feed or with a controlled release fertilizer incorporated into the compost before use.

Making your own composts

John Innes Seed and Potting composts are still excellent for growing a wide range of plants. Indeed, many gardeners still prefer them. Ideally, the loam used should be derived from stacked turf but good garden soil will give satisfactory results.

Soil can be sterilized in small quantities in the microwave oven or with boiling water but, if you're prepared to pick out a few weeds, it's not really necessary.

The original formula uses peat but I have successfully substituted coir compost, leaf-mould or sieved garden compost.

Seed compost

2 parts loam, 1 part leaf-mould or compost, 1 part sharp sand. Add to each bushel (4 two-gallon buckets), 1½oz. superphosphate, ¾oz. lime.

Potting compost

JOHN INNES NO. 1
7 parts loam, 3 parts leaf-mould or compost, 2 parts sharp sand. Add to each bushel (4 two-gallon buckets), 4oz. John Innes Base Fertilizer, ¾oz lime.

JOHN INNES NO. 2
This is used for plants that will be in the pots rather longer and is made in the same way except that the amount of fertilizer is doubled.

JOHN INNES NO. 3
This is for long-term potting and here the fertilizer is trebled.

Alpine compost

Alpines require a very well-drained compost. I make mine using equal parts of soil, garden compost and coarse horticultural grit. No fertilizer is added. Lime may be necessary if your soil is acid.

Plants for Problem Places

The very first rule for successful planting is to ensure that you choose the right plant for each particular situation.

There's never a place in the garden that won't grow *anything*. Even the darkest, driest spot will support some form of life though in extreme cases the choices are naturally fewer.

Always start by trying to alleviate the problem as far as possible. Try to prune overhanging trees judiciously to improve light admission. Improve heavy soil with plenty of coarse grit and light, dry soil with barrowloads of bulky organic matter.

Naturally, it always pays to give the plants the best possible chance so you should also make sure that you coddle them with loving care until they're established with a big enough root system to look after themselves.

Plants for Moist Shade

Trees

Acer cappadocicum
 – *griseum*
 – *negundo*
 – *platanoides*
 – *pseudoplatanus*
 – *saccharinum*
Alnus
Betula nigra
 – *pendula*
Cercidiphyllum japonicum
Crataegus, all forms
Fraxinus in variety
Ilex aquifolium
 × *altaclerensis*
Populus
Prunus padus forms
Pterocarya
Quercus
Salix
Sorbus

Shrubs

Acer palmatum
 – – 'Atropurpureum'
Aucuba japonica
 – – 'Picturata'
 – – 'Salicifolia'
 – – 'Variegata'
Camellia
Cephalotaxus harringtonia drupacea
Cercidiphyllum japonicum

Clethra alnifolia paniculata
Cornus varieties
Danäe racemosa
Daphne laureola
Decaisnea fargesii
Elaeagnus angustifolia
– *commutata*
– × *ebbingei*
– *pungens* 'Maculata'
– *umbellata* var. *parvifolia*
Euonymus fortunei
Fatsia japonica
Fothergilla major
– *monticola*
Gaultheria procumbens
– *shallon*
Hamamelis
Hydrangea
Hypericum calycinum
Ilex
Ligustrum
Osmanthus × *burkwoodii*
– *decorus*
Pachysandra terminalis
Pernettya
Pieris
Prunus laurocerasus
Rhododendron
Rubus cockburnianus
– *thibetanus* 'Silver Fern'
– *tricolor*
– Tridel Benenden
– *ulmifolius* 'Bellidiflorus'
Ruscus aculeatus
Salix
Sambucus
Sarcococca humilis
Skimmia
Spiraea thunbergii
– × *vanhouttei*
Stachyurus praecox
Staphylea in variety
Symphoricarpos

Viburnum davidii
– *opulus*
– *rhytidophyllum*

Conifers

Metasequoia
Picea
Taxus

Herbaceous perennials

Alchemilla mollis
Aruncus sylvester
Asplenium scolopendrium
Astilbe
Athyrium filix-femina
Caltha palustris 'Plena'
Cimicifuga
Convallaria majalis
Dicentra
Dryopteris pseudomas
Endymion nonscriptus
Erythronium revolutum
Gentiana asclepiadea
Haberlea rhodopensis
Helleborus
Hosta
Iris sibirica
Ligularia przewalskii
Lilium martagon
Lythrum
Matteuccia struthiopteris
Monarda
Peltiphyllum peltatum
Polygonum
Polystichum setiferum
Primula (candelabra types)
Ramonda
Rodgersia
Sasa veitchii
Saxifraga fortunei
Smilacina racemosa
Symphytum

Tricyrtis (Toad lily)
Trollius
Uvularia
Vinca
Viola

Plants for Dry Shade

Trees

Acer campestre
 – *ginnala*
 – *platanoides* in variety
 – *pseudoplatanus*
Aesculus
Alnus
Amelanchier lamarckii
Betula
Caragana arborescens
Crataegus prunifolia
Gleditsia triacanthos
Populus
Quercus cerris
 – *ilex*
Robinia (except 'Frisia')
Sorbus aucuparia

Shrubs

Amelanchier lamarckii
Aucuba
Berberis
Buxus sempervirens
Cotoneaster
Danäe racemosa
Euonymus
Garrya elliptica
Hippophae rhamnoides
Ilex
Lonicera pileata
Mahonia
Osmanthus decorus
Pachysandra terminalis

Pittosporum tenuifolium
Prunus laurocerasus
Rubus calycinoides
 – × 'Betty Ashburner'
 – *tricolor*
 – *ulmifolius* 'Bellidiflorus'
Ruscus aculeatus
Skimmia
Symphoricarpos

Conifers

Cephalotaxus
Juniperus media 'Pfitzeriana'
Podocarpus
Taxus

Perennials

Acanthus
Ajuga
Alchemilla mollis
Aquilegia
Arum
Arundinaria

Astrantia
Bergenia
Brunnera macrophylla
Campanula
Carex
Cortaderia
Corydalis
Cyclamen neapolitanum
Dicentra eximia
 – formosa
Digitalis
Epimedium perralderianum
Euphorbia amygdaloides var. robbiae
Geranium macrorrhizum
 – nodosum
 – phaeum
Helleborus
Heuchera
Holcus mollis 'Variegatus'
Iris foetidissima
Lamium
Liriope muscari
Lunaria annua
Meconopsis cambrica
Melissa
Milium
Polygonatum
Polypodium vulgare (fern)
Pulmonaria
Salvia
Sambucus
Santolina
Smyrnium perfoliatum
Tellima grandiflora
Teucrium
Thalictrum
Tiarella
Tolmiea
Valeriana
Vinca
Viola labradorica
Waldsteinia ternata

Plants for Seaside Areas

Trees

Acer pseudoplatanus
Arbutus unedo
Atriplex halimus
Castanea sativa
Crataegus all forms
Escallonia 'Crimson Spire'
 – ingramii
Eucalyptus gunnii
 – niphophila
Fraxinus angustifolia
 – excelsior
Fuchsia
Griselinia littoralis
Ilex × altaclerensis
 – aquifolium
Laurus nobilis
Phillyrea latifolia
Populus alba
 – canescens
 – tremula
Prunus padus
Quercus cerris
 – ilex
 – petraea
 – robur
 – × turneri
Rosmarinus officinalis
Salix
Sorbus aria
 – aucuparia

Shrubs

Arbutus
Arundinaria
Atriplex canescens
 – halimus
Aucuba
Baccharis halimifolia
 – patagonica

Buddleia davidii forms
 – globosa
Bupleurum fruticosum
Chamaerops humilis
Choisya ternata
Cistus
Colutea
Coprosma lucida
Cordyline australis
 – indivisa
Corokia cotoneaster
 – × virgata
Cotoneaster
Cytisus
Elaeagnus × ebbingei
 – commutata
 – glabra
 – pungens
Ephedra
Erica arborea alpina
 – lusitanica
 – × veitchii
Escallonia
Euonymus fortunei
 – japonicus
Fabiana imbricata 'Prostrata'
Fuchsia magellanica
Garrya elliptica
Genista
Griselinia
Halimium
Halimodendron halodendron
Hebe
Hippophae rhamnoides
Hydrangea macrophylla
Ilex aquifolium
Lavandula spica
Lavatera olbia
Leycesteria formosa
Lonicera pileata
Lycium
Myrica cerifera
Olearia
Ozothamnus

Pachysandra insignis
Parahebe
Phormium tenax
Pittosporum
Prunus spinosa
Pyracantha
Rhamnus alaternus
Ribes
Rosa
Rosmarinus officinalis
Salix
Sambucus racemosa
Santolina
Senecio
Sibiraea laevigata
Spartium
Spiraea
Tamarix
Ulex
Viburnum
Yucca

Conifers

Cupressus arizonica
 – macrocarpa
Juniperus
Picea omorika
Pinus nigra var. maritima
 – sylvestris

Herbaceous perennials

Achillea
Allium
Alstroemeria
Anthemis
Anthericum
Artemisia
Aster
Bergenia
Campanula

Centaurea
Colutea
Crocosmia
Dianthus
Dierama pulcherrimum
Echinops
Elymus arenarius
Erigeron
Erodium
Eryngium
Euphorbia
Filipendula hexapetala
Geranium
Gypsophila
Heuchera
Iris
Libertia
Limonium
Linaria
Lychnis flos-jovis
Melissa
Mimulus
Morina
Nerine
Oenothera
Origanum
Penstemon
Phygelius
Physostegia
Potentilla
Pulsatilla
Ruta
Salvia
Santolina
Scabiosa
Schizostylis
Scrophularia
Sedum
Sisyrinchium
Stachys
Stokesia
Tritonia
Veronica
Zantedeschia

Plants for Hot, Sunny and Dry Places

Trees

Acer campestre
Calocedrus decurrens
Genista aetnensis
Gleditsia triacanthos

Shrubs

Abelia
Artemisia arborescens
Atriplex halimus
Berberis
Buddleia
Buxus
Caryopteris
 × clandonensis
Ceanothus
Ceratostigma willmottianum
Cistus
Clerodendrum trichotomum
Colutea arborescens
Convolvulus cneorum
Corokia cotoneaster
Coronilla glauca
Cotoneaster
Cytisus
Dorycnium hirsutum
Elsholtzia stauntonii
Escallonia
Euonymus
Genista
Hebe
Hedysarum multijugum
Hibiscus syriacus
Hippophae rhamnoides
Kolkwitzia amabilis 'Pink Cloud'
Lavandula
Olearia
Perovskia 'Blue Spire'
Philadelphus

Phlomis fruiticosa
Phormium in variety
Phygelius capensis
Piptanthus laburnifolius
Potentilla
Prunus amygdalus
 – tenella
Rhus
Ribes
Rosmarinus
Sambucus
Santolina
Senecio
Spartium junceum
Spiraea
Symphoricarpos
Tamarix
Teucrium fruticans
Ulex
Yucca

Conifers

Juniperus communis
 – media
Pinus mugo
Taxus baccata
Thuja

Herbaceous perennials

Acaena
Acanthus spinosus
Achillea
Agapanthus
Allium
Alstroemeria aurantiaca
Alyssum saxatile 'Compactum'
Anaphalis margaritacea
Antennaria
Anthemis tinctoria
Arabis
Armeria
Artemisia

Asphodeline lutea
Ballota
Bergenia
Bupleurum falcatum
Calamintha
Carex morrowii 'Evergold'
Catananche caerulea 'Major'
Centaurea dealbata
Centranthus
Cerastium
Ceratostigma plumbaginoides
Cestrum
Chamaemelum nobile
Cheiranthus
Chrysanthemopsis hosmariense
Cichorium
Cirsium rivulare
Commelina
Convolvulus sabatius
Coreopsis
Cotula
Crambe cordifolia
Crepis incana
Crinum
Crocosmia
Cynara
Dianthus
Diascia
Dictamnus
Dierama
Draba aizoides
Echinops ritro
Epilobium canum
Eriophyllum
Erodium
Eryngium
Erysimum
Euphorbia coralloides
 – characias subsp.
 – cyparissias
 – dulcis
 – myrsinites
 – polychroma
 – seguieriana

Ferula communis
Foeniculum
Galactites tomentosa
Gaura
Geranium
Gladiolus papilio
Glaucium
Grindelia
Gypsophila
Haplopappus
Helianthemum
Helichrysum lanatum
Hypericum
Iberis 'Snowflake'
Incarvillea delavayi
Indigofera gerardiana
Ipheion uniflorum
Iris foetidissima
  – *germanica*
  – 'Green Spot'
  – *pallida*
  – *unguicularis*
Kniphofia
Leptinella squalida

Liatris 'Kobold'
Libertia formosa
  – *grandiflora*
  – *peregrinans*
Linaria
Linum
Lychnis coronaria
  – *flos-jovis*
Marrubium
Melissa
Minuartia
Moltkia petraea
Nepeta gigantea
  – *mussinii*
Nerine bowdenii
Oenothera
Onopordum
Origanum rotundifolium
Osteospermum
Othonnopsis
Papaver orientale
Penstemon barbatus
Phlox douglasii
  – *subulata*
Potentilla
Pulsatilla vulgaris
Raoulia
Romneya
Rosmarinus officinalis
Ruta graveolens
Salvia patens
Santolina corsica
Saponaria ocymoides
Sedum
Sempervivum
Sideritis
Silene maritima
Sisyrinchium striatum
Stachys
Stipa
Strobilanthes
Thymus
Tulipa
Verbascum

Cold and Windy

Trees

Acer campestre
 – *negundo*
 – *platanoides*
   'Cleveland'
   'Drummondii'
   'Globosum'
   'Laciniatum'
   'Olmstead'
   'Royal Red'
   'Schwedleri'
 – *pseudoplatanus*
   'Erectum'
   'Leopoldii'
   'Spaethii'
   'Worleei'
Alnus glutinosa
 – *incana*
Betula
Carpinus betulus
 – 'Fastigiata'
 – 'Purpurea'
Corylus
Crataegus
Fagus sylvatica
 – 'Asplenifolia'
 – 'Dawyck'
Fraxinus excelsior
Gleditsia triacanthos
Laburnum
Populus
Quercus
Sorbus aria
 – *aucuparia*
 – *intermedia*
Tilia cordata
Ulmus angustifolia
 – 'Cornubiensis'

Shrubs

Actinidia kolomikta
Arctostaphylos uva-ursi
Arundinaria japonica
Berberis
Buddleia
Calluna vulgaris
Caragana arborescens
Chaenomeles
Chamaedaphne calyculata
Clematis viticella
Clethra alnifolia
Colutea arborescens
Cornus
Corylus
Cotinus coggygria
Cotoneaster
Deutzia
Elaeagnus
Euonymus alatus
Gaultheria shallon
Hamamelis virginiana
Hippophae rhamnoides
Hydrangea paniculata 'Grandiflora'
Hypericum calycinum
Ilex
Jasminum nudiflorum
Kalmia angustifolia
 – *latifolia*
Kerria
Lavatera olbia
Ledum groenlandicum
Leucothöe fontanesiana
Ligustrum ovalifolium
Lonicera involucrata
 – *pileata*
Mahonia
Myrica gale
Pachysandra terminalis
Pernettya
Philadelphus
Pieris floribunda
Potentilla

Prunus spinosa
Rhododendron caucasicum
 – ponticum
 – yakushimanum
Rosa rugosa
Ruscus
Salix
Sambucus nigra
Spartium junceum
Spiraea
Symphoricarpos
Tamarix
Ulex
Viburnum lantana
 – rhytidophyllum
Wisteria floribunda

Conifers

Chamaecyparis nootkatensis
 – obtusa
 – pisifera
Cryptomeria japonica
Cupressocyparis leylandii
Ginkgo biloba
Juniperus
Picea abies
 – breweriana
 – omorika
Pinus
Taxus
Thuja
Tsuga canadensis

Herbaceous perennials

Acaena
Achillea filipendulina
Ajuga reptans
Allium
Anemone × hybrida
Arundinaria
Bergenia
Campanula carpatica

Cimicifuga foetida
Coreopsis verticillata
Dryas octopetala
Echinops ritro
Helleborus niger
Hesperis matronalis
Iris sibirica
Malva moschata
Miscanthus
Nepeta × faassenii
Osmunda regalis
Phalaris arundinacea
Phlox subulata
Polygonum affine
Primula
Pulmonaria saccharata
Sempervivum
Stipa gigantea
Tanacetum vulgare
Tiarella wherryi

Waterlogged Sites

Trees

Acer negundo
Alnus
Amelanchier
Betula
Crataegus oxyacantha
Fraxinus
Liquidambar
Liriodendron
Magnolia virginiana
Mespilus germanica
Nothofagus antarctica
Parrotia
Populus
Pterocarya
Pyrus
Quercus palustris
Salix
Sorbus aucuparia

Shrubs

Amelanchier lamarckii
Andromeda polifolia
Aronia
Calycanthus
Cephalanthus occidentalis
Clethra
Cornus alba
 – *baileyi*
 – *stolonifera*
Gaultheria shallon
Hippophae rhamnoides
Ilex verticillata
Lindera benzoin
Myrica cerifera
 – *gale*
Neillia longiracemosa
Parrotia persica
Pernettya
Philadelphus

Photinia villosa
Physocarpus opulifolius
Prunus spinosa
Rhamnus frangula
Rhododendron Hardy Hybrids
Salix × *balfourii*
 – *caprea*
 – *humilis*
 – *integra*
 – *purpurea*
 – *repens*
Sambucus
Sorbaria
Spiraea × *billiardii*
 – × *vanhouttei*
 – *veitchii*
Symphoricarpos
Vaccinium
Viburnum dentatum
 – *lantana*
 – *lentago*
 – *opulus rhytidophyllum*

Conifers

Abies
Cedrus deodara
Metasequoia glyptostroboides
Picea sitchensis
Taxodium ascendens
 – *distichum*

Herbaceous perennials

Acorus
Ajuga reptans
Anaphalis margaritacea
Astilbe
Butomus umbellatus
Caltha
Cardamine pratensis
Carex elata 'Aurea'
 – *pendula*
 – *riparia*

Darmera
Dodecatheon meadia
Eupatorium
Euphorbia palustris
Filipendula
Geranium
Glyceria maxima
Gunnera manicata
Hemerocallis
Houttuynia
Inula
Iris ensata
– laevigata
– pseudacorus
– versicolor
Ligularia
Lobelia
Luzula maxima
Lysichiton
Lythrum
Miscanthus
Monarda didyma
Myosotis
Persicaria bistorta
– campanulatum
– milletii
Petasites japonicus
Pontederia
Primula bulleyana
– florindae
– japonica
– pulverulenta
Ranunculus acris
– constantinopolitanus 'Flore Plenus'
Rodgersia
Sasa veitchii
Senecio smithii
Spartina
Thalictrum flavum
Trollius
Verbena corymbosa
Zantedeschia

Acid Soils

Trees

Acer negundo
– rubrum
Ailanthus altissima
Betula
Castanea
Cercidiphyllum japonicum
Cercis
Cornus kousa
Crataegus monogyna
Embothrium coccineum
Eucryphia
Fagus sylvatica
Gleditsia
Halesia
Ilex aquifolium
Koelreuteria paniculata
Liquidambar styraciflua
Populus alba
– canescens
– tremula
Quercus cerris
– robur
Robinia
Sorbus × hybrida
– intermedia

Shrubs

Acer palmatum 'Dissectum'
Amelanchier canadensis
Arctostaphylos
Baptisia australis
Berberis vulgaris
Calluna vulgaris
Camellia
Cassiope
Corylopsis
Cryptomeria japonica 'Vilmoriniana'
Daboecia cantabrica
Desfontainia

Dicentra
Enkianthus
Erica
Fothergilla monticola
Gaultheria
Halesia
Hamamelis mollis
Ilex aquifolium
Kalmia latifolia
Lapageria rosea
Ledum
Leucothöe
Lilium pardalinum
Lycium barbarum
Magnolia stellata
Osmunda regalis
Pachysandra
Parrotia persica
Pernettya
Pieris
Rhamnus frangula
Rhododendron (incl. Azalea)
Salix × balfourii
 - caprea
 - cinerea
Sambucus nigra
 - racemosa
Sarcococca
Skimmia
Staphylea
Tricyrtis
Ulmus pumila
Viburnum opulus

Conifers

Abies
Chamaecyparis
Cryptomeria japonica 'Elegans'
Juniperus
Larix
Lawsoniana
Picea

Pinus nigra
 - sylvestris
Taxodium
Taxus baccata

Herbaceous perennials

Corydalis
Dactylorrhiza elata
Disporum smithii
Epimedium
Erythronium revolutum
Gentiana sino-ornata
Kirengeshoma palmata
Lilium davidii
 - tigrinum
Liriope muscari
Lupinus 'Russell Hybrids'
Meconopsis betonicifolia
Ourisia
Primula vulgaris
 - vulgaris elatior
Rhodohypoxis
Tricyrtis hirta
Trillium grandiflorum
Tropaeolum

Chalky Soils

Trees

Acer campestre
 - cappadocicum
 - griseum
 - negundo forms
 - platanoides
 - pseudoplatanus
Aesculus
Ailanthus
Amelanchier
Betula
Caragana

Carpinus betulus
Catalpa
Cercis siliquastrum
Corylus
Crataegus oxyacantha
Fagus sylvatica
Fraxinus excelsior
  – ornus
Gleditsia
Juglans
Laburnum
Liriodendron
Magnolia kobus
Malus
Morus nigra
Paulownia
Platanus
Populus alba
  – canescens
Prunus all 'Japanese Cherries'
Pyrus
Robinia
Salix
Sophora
Sorbus aria
  – hybrida
  – intermedia
Tilia
Ulmus

Shrubs

Aesculus parviflora
Arbutus
Arundinaria
Baccharis halimifolia
Berberis
Buddleia davidii
Buxus
Callicarpa
Caragana arborescens
Catalpa
Ceanothus

Choisya
Cistus
Clematis
Clerododendrum trichotomum
Colutea
Cornus mas
Cotoneaster
Cytisus nigricans
Daphne mezereum
Deutzia
Dipelta floribunda
Elaeagnus
Erica carnea
Escallonia
Eucryphia
Euonymus
Forsythia
Fuchsia
Genista cinerea
Hebe
Hedera
Helianthemum nummularium
Hibiscus syriacus
Hydrangea villosa
Hypericum
Ilex
Indigofera
Kerria
Kolkwitzia amabilis
Laurus nobilis
Ligustrum
Lonicera
Magnolia kobus
Mahonia aquifolium
Olearia
Osmanthus
Paeonia delavayi
  – – lutea
Philadelphus
Phillyrea
Phlomis
Photinia serratifolia
Pittosporum
Potentilla fruticosa

Prunus laurocerasus
Pyracantha
Rhus
Ribes
Romneya
Rosa
Rosmarinus
Rubus tricolor
Salix
Sambucus
Santolina
Sarcococca
Senecio
Spartium junceum
Spiraea japonica
– nipponica
Stachyurus praecox
Staphylea
Symphoricarpus
Syringa vulgaris
Tamarix
Teucrium
Ulex
Viburnum
Vinca
Weigela
Yucca

Conifers

Juniperus communis
– media
Pinus mugo
– nigra
Taxus baccata
Thuya

Herbaceous perennials

Acanthus
Alyssum
Anemone
Anthemis cupaniana
Aubrieta deltoidea

Campanula cochleariifolia
– glomerata
Dianthus
Eremurus
Iris germanica
Linaria purpurea
Paeonia
Papaver orientale
Phlomis
Platycodon
Primula veris
Prunella
Pulsatilla vulgaris
Pyrethrum
Salvia sclarea
Saponaria
Saxifraga umbrosa
Scabiosa caucasica
Sedum spectabile
Thymus vulgaris
Tradescantia
Verbascum bombyciferum
Veronica

Plants for Clay Soils

Trees

Acer
Aesculus
Alnus
Betula
Carpinus
Corylus
Crataegus
Eucalyptus
Fraxinus
Ilex
Laburnum
Malus
Ostrya
Populus
Prunus

Pyrus
Quercus
Salix
Sorbus
Tilia

Shrubs

Abelia
Aralia elata
Aronia
Aucuba japonica
Berberis
Chaenomeles
Choisya ternata
Colutea
Cornus
Corylus avellana
Cotinus coggygria
Cotoneaster
Crataegus
Cytisus
Escallonia
Eucalyptus
Forsythia
Genista
Hamamelis
Hedera helix
Hibiscus syriacus
Hypericum
Kerria
Lonicera
Magnolia
Mahonia
Osmanthus
Philadelphus
Pieris floribunda
Potentilla
Prunus cistena
  – laurocerasus
Pyracantha
Rhamnus frangula
Rhododendron
Ribes sanguineum

Rosa
Rubus
Salix daphnoides
Senecio greyi
Skimmia
Spiraea 'Arguta'
Symphoricarpos
Syringa
Viburnum plicatum
Weigela florida

Conifers

Abies
Chamaecyparis
Juniperus
Larix
Picea breweriana
Pinus
Taxodium distichum
Taxus
Thuja

Herbaceous perennials

Aconitum
Ajuga
Alopecurus
Anemone japonica
  – nemorosa
Arundinaria
Aster
Camassia leichtlinii
Campanula
Carex
Cephalaria
Crocosmia masonorum
Darmera
Deschampsia
Digitalis
Doronicum plantagineum
Echinops
Epimedium
Eranthis hyemalis

Erigeron
Euphorbia amygdaloides var. robbiae
Filipendula
Gentiana
Geranium
Helenium autumnale
Helleborus
Hemerocallis
Hosta
Inula
Iris
Lamium
Levisticum
Ligularia
Lonicera
Lysimachia clethroides
Lythrum
Miscanthus
Molinia
Monarda
Narcissus
Oenothera
Panicum
Peltiphyllum
Persicaria affinis
Petasites
Phyllostachys
Physalis
Physostegia
Podophyllum emodi
Polemonium
Polygonatum
Primula
Prunella webbiana
Ranunculus
Rheum
Rodgersia
Rudbeckia
Salvia
Sasa veitchii
Saxifraga × urbium
Sidalcea
Solidago
Spartina

Symphytum
Trachystemon
Tradescantia
Waldsteinia

Shrubs and Climbers for North and East Facing Walls

Shrubs

Acradenia frankliniae
Agapetes serpens
Azara microphylla
 – petiolaris
Berberis × stenophylla
Camellia japonica
 – reticulata
 – saluenensis
 – sasanqua
 – × williamsii
Chaenomeles
Choisya ternata
Crinodendron hookerianum
 – patagua
Daphne gnidium
 – × hybrida
 – odora
Desfontainea spinosa
Drimys winteri
Eriobotrya japonica
Eucryphia cordifolia
 – × intermedia
 – × nymansensis
Euonymus fortunei
Garrya elliptica
 – × thuretii
Grevillea rosmarinifolia
Ilex georgei
 – insignis
 – latifolia
Illicum anisatum

Itea ilicifolia
Jasminum humile
– nudiflorum
Kerria japonica
Lomatia myricoides
Mahonia japonica
– lomariifolia
– × media
Mitraria coccinea
Osmanthus delavayi
– yunnanensis
Photinia serrulata
Piptanthus laburnifolius
Pyracantha
Ribes laurifolium
Rubus henryi
– lambertianus
Schima argentea
Viburnum grandiflorum

Climbers

Akebia quinata
Aristolochia macrophylla
Azara microphylla
Berchemia racemosa
Celastrus orbiculatus
– scandens
Chaenomeles
Cotoneaster horizontalis
Escallonia
Euonymus fortunei
Forsythia suspensa
Garrya elliptica
Hedera canariensis 'Variegata'
– colchica
– – 'Dentata Aurea'
– helix
– hibernica
Hydrangea anomala
– petiolaris
Jasminum officinale 'Grandiflorum'
– × stephanense
Lathyrus

Lonicera × americana
– japonica
Muehlenbeckia complexa
Parthenocissus
Pileostegia viburnoides
Polygonum baldschuanicum
Rosa
Schisandra grandiflora
Schizophragma hydrangeoides
– integrifolium
Vitis

Shrubs and Climbers for South and West Walls

Shrubs

Abeliophyllum distichum
Acacia
Buddleia
Carpenteria californica
Ceanothus
Choisya ternata
Clianthus puniceus
Fremontodendron

Climbers

Abeliophyllum distichum
Abutilon megapotamicum
Acacia dealbata
Actinidia chinensis
– kolomikta
Akebia quinata
Aristolochia macrophylla
Buddleia colvilei
– fallowiana alba
Campsis grandiflora
Ceanothus
Chimonanthus
Clematis
Clianthus puniceus

Cobaea scandens
Cytisus battandieri
Eccremocarpus scaber
Escallonia
Humulus lupulus 'Aureus'
Hydrangea petiolaris
Ipomoea
Itea ilicifolia
Leptospermum scoparium
Lippia citriodora
Lonicera 'Dropmore Scarlet'
 – × *tellmanniana*
Magnolia grandiflora
Myrtus
Passiflora caerulea
Phygelius capensis
Piptanthus laburnifolius
Prunus triloba 'Multiplex'
Solanum crispum 'Glasnevin'
Thunbergia alata
Trachelospermum jasminoides
Viburnum burkwoodii
Vitis
Wisteria

Plants for Scent

Trees

Acacia dealbata
Aesculus hippocastanum
Azara microphylla
Cladrastis lutea
 – *sinensis*
Crataegus monogyna 'Stricta'
Drimys winteri
Eucryphia
Fraxinus sieboldiana
 – *ornus*
Gordonia
Laburnum alpinum
 – *vossii*
 – *watereri*
Magnolia fraseri
 – *kobus*
 – *macrophylla*
 – *obovata*
 – *salicifolia*
Malus angustifolia
 – *baccata mandschurica*
 – *coronaria* 'Charlottae'
 – *floribunda*
 – *hupehensis*
 – × *robusta*
Michelia doltsopa
 – *figo*
Myrceugenia exsucca
Myrtus apiculata
Pittosporum eugenioides
Poliothyrsis sinensis
Prunus 'Amanogawa'
 – *conradinae*
 – 'Jo-nioi'
 – *lusitanica*
 – *padus* 'Grandiflora'
 – *serrulata*
 – 'Shirotae'
 – × *yedoensis*

Robinia pseudoacacia
Styrax japonica
Tilia × *euchlora*
  – *europaea*
  – *oliveri*
  – *petiolaris*
  – *platyphyllos*
  – *tomemtosa*

Shrubs

Abelia chinensis
  – × *grandiflora*
  – *triflora*
Alangium
Azara lanceolata
  – *petiolaris*
Berberis buxifolia
  – *sargentiana*
  – *stenophylla*
  – *vulgaris*
Bruckenthalia spiculifolia
Buddleia
Buxus sempervirens
Camellia sasanqua
Ceanothus 'Gloire de Versailles'
Chimonanthus praecox
Chionanthus virginicus
Choisya ternata
Cionura erecta
Citrus
Clematis heracleifolia
Clethra acuminata
  – *alnifolia* 'Paniculata'
  – *barbinervis*
  – *fargesii*
Colletia armata
  – *cruciata*
Cordyline australis
Corokia cotoneaster
Coronilla glauca
  – *valentina*
Corylopsis

Cytisus battandieri
  – 'Porlock'
  – × *praecox*
  – *purgans*
Daphne
Datura suaveolens
Deutzia compacta
  – × *elegantissima*
Edgeworthia papyrifera
Elaeagnus angustifolia
  – *commutata*
  – × *ebbingei*
  – *glabra*
  – *macrophylla*
  – *umbellata*
Erica arborea 'Alpina'
  – × *darleyensis*
  – *lusitanica*
  – × *veitchii*
Escallonia 'Donard Gem'
Eucryphia milliganii
Euonymus sachalinensis
Eupatorium ligustrinum
Fothergilla gardenii
  – *major*
  – *monticola*
Freylinia lanceolata
Gaultheria forrestii
Genista aetnensis
  – *cinerea*
  – *monosperma*
  – *tinctoria*
Hakea microcarpa
Hamamelis mollis
Hoheria glabrata
  – *lyallii*
Itea ilicifolia
  – *virginica*
Jasminum humile 'Revolutum'
  – *wallichianum*
Lavandula
Ligustrum quihoui
Lomatia myricoides
Lonicera

Luculia gratissima
Lupinus arboreus
Magnolia
Mahonia aquifolium
 – japonica
 – × media
 – – 'Charity'
Myrtus communis
Olearia × haastii

 – ilicifolia
 – macrodonta
 – odorata
 – rani
Osmanthus
× Osmarea burkwoodii
Paeonia × lemoinei
Paulownia fargesii
 – lilacina
Perovskia 'Blue Spire'
Petteria ramentacea
Philadelphus
Pimelea prostrata
Pittosporum patulum
 – tenuifolium
 – tobira
 – undulatum
Poncirus trifoliata
Prunus mume
Ptelea trifoliata
Pterostyrax
Pyracantha
Rhododendron
Ribes alpinum
 – fasciculatum
 – gayanum
 – odoratum
Romneya
Rosa
Rubus 'Tridel Benenden'
Sarcococca
Skimmia japonica 'Fragrans'
 – japonica 'Rubella'
 – laureola
Spartium junceum

Syringa
Ulex europaeus
Viburnum
Yucca filamentosa
 – flaccida
Zenobia pulverulenta

Herbaceous perennials

Adenophora liliifolia
Asphodeline lutea
Calanthe discolor
Cestrum parqui
Clematis heracleifolia var. davidiana
 – recta
Convallaria majalis
Cosmos atrosanguineus
Crambe cordifolia
Dianthus
Dictamnus albus
Hemerocallis lilio-asphodelus
Hosta 'Honeybells'
Houttuynia cordata
Iris graminea
 – hoogiana
 – pallida
 – unguicularis
Lonicera japonica 'Halliana'
Lunaria rediviva
Maianthemum
Monarda
Paeonia lactiflora
Phlox maculata
 – paniculata
 – pilosa
Polygonum polystachyum
Primula vulgaris
Tellima grandiflora rubra
 – odorata
Verbena
Viola 'Maggie Mott'
 – 'Moonlight'
 – odorata

Climbers

Abeliophyllum distichum
Acacia dealbata
Actindia chinensis
 – *polygama*
Akebia quinata
Clematis armandii
 – *cirrhosa balearica*
 – *flammula*
 – *montana*
 – *paniculata*
 – *rehderiana*
 – *uncinata*
Decumaria sinensis
Holboellia latifolia
Itea ilicifolia
Jasminum azoricum
 – *beesianum*
 – *officinale*
 – *polyanthum*
 – × *stephanense*
Lardizabala biternata
Lippia citriodora
Lonicera × *americana*
 – *caprifolium*
 – *etrusca*
 – × *heckrottii*
 – *japonica* 'Halliana'
 – *periclymenum*
   repens
 – 'Serotina'
Mandevilla suaveolens
Myrtus
Stauntonia hexaphylla
Viburnum × *burkwoodii*
Vitis coignetiae
 – *riparia*
Wattakaka sinensis
Wisteria sinensis

Bulbs

Cardiocrinum giganteum
Crinum × *powellii*
Cyclamen hederifolium
 – *purpurascens*
Galanthus
Galtonia
Gladiolus tristis
Hermodactylus tuberosus
Hyacinthus orientalis
Lilium
Narcissus

Plants with Aromatic Foliage

Trees

Atherosperma moschatum
Cercidiphyllum japonicum
Cinnamomum camphora
Clerodendrum
Eucalyptus
Juglans
Laurelia serrata
Laurus nobilis
Phellodendron
Populus balsamifera
 – *trichocarpa*
Salix pentandra
 – *triandra*
Sassafras albidum
Umbellularia californica

Shrubs

Artemisia arborescens
Camphorosma monspeliaca
Caryopteris clandonensis
Choisya ternata
Cistus
Clerodendrum

Coleonema
Comptonia peregrina
Elsholtzia stauntonii
Escallonia illinita
 – laevis
 – macrantha
 – rubra
Eucalyptus gunnii
Gaultheria procumbens
Hebe cupressoides
Helichrysum plicatum
 – serotinum
Hypericum hircinum
Illicium
Laurus nobilis
Lavandula spica
Leptospermum liversidgei
Lindera
Lippia citriodora
Myrica
Myrtus communis
Olearia ilicifolia
 – mollis
 – moschata
Orixa japonica
Perovskia 'Blue Spire'

Phlomis fruticosa
Prostranthera
Ptelea trifoliata
Rhododendron
Ribes sanguineum
 – viburnifolium
Rosa eglanteria
Rosmarinus officinalis
Ruta graveolens
Santolina
Tasmannia aromatica

Herbaceous perennials

Agastache foeniculum
Anthemis punctata cupaniana
Delphinium brunonianum
Geranium endressii
 – macrorrhizum
Meum athamanticum
Morina longifolia
Nepeta × faassenii
Salvia glutinosa
 – microphylla
Smilacina racemosa

Plants for Wildlife

Attracting wildlife into the garden helps control pests and will add an enormous amount of colour, movement and interest.

Birds can be attracted with trees and shrubs for perching on and nesting in and with plants to provide food, especially in winter.

Bees, butterflies and many other insects can be brought into the garden by providing food plants in particular. Breeding colonies can best be established on native plants which many of us gardeners class as 'weeds'. So you may prefer to badger the local council into not cutting the grass verges outside rather than filling your garden with stinging nettles. It's much more effective anyway.

Trees and Shrubs that Attract Birds

Trees

Alnus
Amelanchier lamarckii
Betula
Crataegus
Malus
Mespilus
Morus
Salix
Sambucus
Sorbus
Staphylea
Syringa
Taxus
Viburnum davidii
 – lantana
 – opulus
 – rhytidophyllum

Shrubs

Arbutus unedo
Arctostaphylos uva-ursi
Aucuba japonica
Berberis
Buddleia
Callicarpa
Chaenomeles
Clerodendrum trichotomum
Colutea
Cornus
Corylus avellana
Cotoneaster
Daphne
Decaisnea
Dorycnium
Elaeagnus

Euonymus europaeus cvs
– *japonicus* 'Latifolius'
– *oxyphyllus*
– *sachalinensis*
– *yedoensis*
Gaultheria
Hedera
Hippophäe rhamnoides
Hypericum inodorum 'Elstead'
– *forrestii*
Ilex
Lavandula 'Hidcote Purple' and
  others that produce seed
Leycesteria formosa
Ligustrum vulgare
Mahonia
Osmanthus
Pernettya
Poncirus trifoliata
Pyracantha
Rhamnus frangula
Rhus typhina
Ribes odoratum
Rubus calycinoides
Ruscus aculeatus
Sambucus
Skimmia japonica 'Foremanii'
– *laureola*
Symphoricarpos
Viburnum
Vitis

Birds are also attracted to many
flower seedheads, including fennel,
teasel, sedum, lemon balm,
lavatera, poppy, antirrhinum,
cosmos, Michaelmas daisy, scabious
and sunflower.

Trees and Shrubs that Attract Bees and Butterflies

Trees

Acer campestre
– *negundo*
– *platanoides*
– 'Royal Red'
– *pseudoplatanus*
– 'Atropurpurea'
Aesculus × *carnea* 'Briotii'
– *hippocastanum*
– *indica*
Ailanthus altissima
Alnus glutinosa (pollen)
– *incana* and forms (pollen)
Betula in variety (pollen)
Caragana arborescens
Castanea sativa
Catalpa bignonioides
Crataegus prunifolia
Fagus (pollen)
Fraxinus excelsior (pollen)
Koelreuteria
Liquidambar styraciflua
Liriodendron tulipifera
Malus
Mespilus germanica
Nothofagus antarctica (pollen)
Populus nigra (pollen)
– *tremula* (pollen)
Prunus avium
– *padus* 'Grandiflora'
– 'Pandora'
– *sargentii*
– 'Shirotae'
– *subhirtella*
– 'Pendula Rubra'
– 'Tai-Haku'
– 'Ukon'
– 'Umeniko'
– × *yedoensis*

Quercus in variety (pollen)
Robinia pseudoacacia
Salix alba
Sorbus aria
 – aucuparia
 – intermedia
Tilia euchlora

Shrubs

Aesculus parviflora
Arbutus
Berberis darwinii
 – × irwinii
 – × stenophylla
 – thunbergii
 – wilsoniae
Buddleia
Buxus
Caryopteris
Ceanothus
Cercis siliquastrum
Chaenomeles speciosa
Cistus
Colutea arborescens
Cornus
Cotoneaster
Cystisus
Daphne mezereum
Elaeagnus
Escallonia
Fuchsia
Hebe
Hypericum androsaemum
 – forestii
Ilex
Laurus nobilis
Lavandula
Ligustrum
Olearia
Perovskia
Physocarpus
Potentilla

Prunus laurocerasus
Pyracantha
Rhamnus frangula
Rhus
Ribes sanguineum
 – speciosum
Salix caprea
 – repens 'Argentea'
Senecio
Skimmia
Spiraea
Staphylea
Stephanandra
Symphoricarpos
Syringa
Tamarix pentandra
Ulex europaeus
Viburnum opulus
 – tinus
Weigela

Perennials and Annuals that Attract Bees and Butterflies

Perennials

Achillea
Ajuga
Alyssum
Anaphalis
Arabis
Armeria
Aster
Aubrieta
Calamintha
Cardamine pratensis
Centaurea
Centranthus ruber
Cephalaria
Ceratostigma
Cheiranthus

Convolvulus
Dendranthema
Dianthus deltoides
Echinacea
Echinops ritro
Erigeron
Eryngium
Erysimum linifolium
Eupatorium
Hebe
Helenium
Helichrysum
Hesperis matronalis
Hyssopus officinalis
Jasione perennis
Knautia arvensis
Liatris
Ligularia clivorum
Lunaria annua
Lychnis
Lysimachia
Lythrum salicaria
Melissa
Mentha
Nepeta faassenii

Persicaria
Phlox
Phuopsis
Primula
Pulicaria dysenterica
Saponaria officinalis
Scabiosa
Sedum spectabile (not 'Autumn Joy')
Solidago
Thymus (not yellow leafed forms)
Verbena bonariensis

Annuals

Alyssum
Calendula
Convolvulus
Dianthus barbatus
Iberis gibraltarica
Limnanthes douglasii
Myosotis
Petunia
Reseda odorata

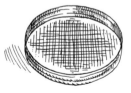

Poisonous Plants

D eciding which plants are poisonous and which can be safely classed as harmless is an impossible task. If you ate enough of almost anything you'd be ill, while small quantities of quite poisonous plants can actually be used as curatives.

To make matters more difficult, there seems to be good evidence for the problems likely to be experienced from eating or handling some plants, including medical histories and detailed symptoms, while for others the evidence is extremely sketchy.

Certainly the plants marked 'highly dangerous' should be treated with extreme care and kept out of the reach of children. Others would only cause harm if large quantities were consumed, or if they were eaten by very young children, or older people with already failing health.

You should certainly not be put off growing lupins, for example, but you should avoid eating the seeds. To suggest not growing tomatoes would be ludicrous, but you should be warned against eating the leaves. Armed with the following warnings and a little common sense, you should have no problems.

* = weeds

Plants to Treat with Care

Common name	Latin name
Amaryllis	*Amaryllis belladonna*
Anemone	*Anemone* spp
Aquilegia (*see* Columbine)	
Aubergine	*Solanum melongena*
Autumn Crocus	*Colchicum autumnale*
Belladonna Lily (*see* Amaryllis)	
*Black Bryony	*Tamus communis*
Black Hellebore (see Christmas Rose)	
*Black Nightshade	*Solanum nigrum*
Bluebell	*Endymion*
Box	*Buxus sempervirens*
Buckthorn	*Frangula alnus*
*Buttercup	*Ranunculus* spp
Castor Oil plant	*Ricinus communis*
Christmas Rose	*Helleborus niger*
Columbine	*Aquilegia* spp
Cotoneaster	*Cotoneaster* spp
*Cuckoo Pint	*Arum maculatum*
Daffodil	*Narcissus* spp
Daphne	*Daphne mezereum*
Datura (*see* Thorn Apple)	
*Deadly Nightshade	*Atropa belladonna*
Delphinium	*Delphinium* spp

Poisonous parts	Effect
bulb	Gastroenteritis.
all parts esp. in flower	Juice is an irritant. Blisters mouth. Gastroenteritis.
leaves	Gastroenteritis.
all parts	Highly dangerous. Gastroenteritis. Convulsions. Respiratory failure.
all parts esp. fruit	Burning mouth. Gastroenteritis.
all parts	Highly dangerous. Delirium. Cardiac and respiratory failure.
bulb	Gastroenteritis.
leaves	Sap is irritant. Sore mouth. Gastroenteritis.
all parts esp. seeds	Burning mouth. Gastroenteritis.
all parts esp. when in flower	Burning mouth. Gastroenteritis.
all parts	Highly dangerous. Sap is irritant. Gastroenteritis. Damages digestive tract, liver and kidneys.
all parts	Diarrhoea and dehydration.
seeds	Slows breathing and heart rate.
berries	Gastroenteritis.
berries	Highly dangerous. Sap irritates mouth. Causes convulsions.
bulb	Gastroenteritis.
all parts esp. berries	Highly dangerous. Sap irritates mouth. Gastroenteritis and convulsions.
all parts	Highly poisonous. Delirium. Heart and respiration failure.
all parts esp. seeds	Abdominal pain, vomiting, constipation.

Common name	Latin name
Dumbcane	*Dieffenbachia sequine*
Egg plant (*see* Aubergine)	
Euphorbia (*see* Spurge)	
Foxglove	*Digitalis purpurea*
Greater Celandine	*Chelidonium majus*
Hellebore (*see* Christmas Rose)	
*Hemlock (*see* Spotted Hemlock)	
Holly	*Ilex aquifolium*
Hyacinth	*Hyacinthus* spp
Ivy	*Hedera helix*
King Cup	*Caltha*
Laburnum	*Laburnum anagyroides*
Larkspur (*see* Delphinium)	
Lily of the Valley	*Convallaria majalis*
*Lords & Ladies (*see* King Cup)	
Lupin	*Lupinius* spp
Marsh Marigold (*see* King Cup)	
Mezereum (*see* Daphne)	
Mistletoe	*Viscum album*
Monkshood	*Aconitum napellus*
Poinsettia	*Euphorbia pulcherrima*
Potato	*Solanum tuberosum*
Primula	*Primula* spp
Privet	*Ligustrum* spp
Rue	*Ruta graveolens*

Poisonous parts	Effect
sap	Irritates lips and mouth and tongue swells.
all parts	Highly dangerous. Abdominal pain. Diarrhoea and vomiting. Heart failure.
all parts	Highly dangerous. Irritating sap. Gastroenteritis.
berries	Gastroenteritis.
bulb	Gastroenteritis.
berries and leaves	Respiratory problems. Gastroenteritis.
all parts esp. in flower	Sap is irritant. Gastroenteritis.
seeds and pods	Highly dangerous. Vomiting. Convulsions. Asphyxia.
all parts	Abdominal pain. Diarrhoea. Heart failure.
seeds	Irritant sap. Gastroenteritis.
leaves and berries	Gastroenteritis. Heart and lung failure.
all parts esp. root	Highly dangerous. Gastroenteritis. Convulsions. Cardiac and respiratory failure.
leaves and sap	Irritant sap causes skin blisters. Gastroenteritis. Delirium.
leaves, stem, fruits, green tubers and sprouts	Burning mouth. Gastroenteritis.
leaves and sap	Irritates skin.
leaves and berries	Drowsiness. Gastroenteritis.
leaves and sap	Irritates skin.

Common name	Latin name
Rhubarb	*Rheum* spp
Snowberry	*Symphoricarpos* spp
Spindletree	*Euonymus* spp
*Spotted Hemlock	*Conium maculatum*
Spurge	*Euphorbia*
Stinking Hellebore	*Helleborus foetidus*
Sweet Pea	*Lathyrus odoratus*
Thorn Apple	*Datura stramonium*
Tomato	*Lycopersicon esculentum*
Virginia Creeper	*Parthenocissus quinquefolia*
Wisteria	*Wisteria floribunda*
*Woody Nightshade	*Solanum dulcamara*
Yew	*Taxus baccata*

Poisonous parts	Effect
leaves	Abdominal pain. Vomiting.
berries	Gastroenteritis.
leaves and fruit	Highly dangerous. Mental confusion. Respiratory failure. Gastroenteritis.
all parts	Highly dangerous. Respiratory failure.
all parts	Sap irritates skin, eyes and mouth. Gastroenteritis.
all parts	Diarrhoea. Dehydration. Convulsions.
seeds	Gastroenteritis.
all parts	Highly dangerous. Delirium. Heart and lung failure.
leaves and stems	Burns throat. Gastroenteritis.
berries	Gastroenteritis.
pods and seeds	Abdominal pain. Vomiting and diarrhoea.
all parts	Highly dangerous. Abdominal pain. Gastroenteritis. Paralysis.
all parts	Highly dangerous. Gastroenteritis. Heart failure.

Fruit Trees

You can do almost anything with fruit trees and, over the years, many different ways of training them have been developed. By using modern rootstocks (see p 170), trees can be kept very small and, if they're pruned to shape too, they can be grown in quite small spaces. Spacings given are approximate because they'll vary depending on the rootstock and the particular fruit you're growing. They're based on apples on semi-dwarfing rootstocks so, if you're growing a larger tree like a plum or cherry or using a more vigorous rootstock you'll have to adjust the spacing.

OPEN CENTRE BUSH

If you want a free-standing tree, this is a traditional way to grow it. The central shoot is removed to encourage bushy growth and to keep the centre of the tree open. The aim is to produce a shape rather like a goblet. On a dwarfing rootstock, apples and pears grown this way need not be too big, though they'll certainly take up more space than most other methods. Plant about 3.5m(12ft) apart.

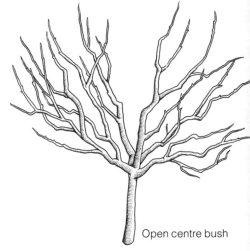

Open centre bush

Dwarf pyramid

DWARF PYRAMID
With this more intensive way of growing, the trees can be planted slightly closer than bushes. The central shoot is maintained and the upper branches are pruned to be somewhat shorter than the lower ones to create a shape rather like a Christmas tree. Plant about 2m(7ft) apart.

ESPALIER
A traditional way to grow apples especially. They make very attractive trees for training on a fence or wall and less often on a post and wire support. Plant about 4.5m (15ft) apart.

STEPOVER
A method that's gaining popularity in small gardens. They're simply single-tier espaliers and are used to edge paths in particular. Plant about 2.5m(8½ft) apart.

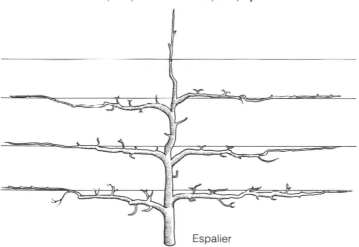

Espalier

CORDON

A popular, space-saving method of training. The trees are grown as a single stem and are planted at an angle to encourage fruiting. The trees are tied in to a wire structure, either free-standing or against a fence or wall. Plant about 75cm (2½ft) apart.

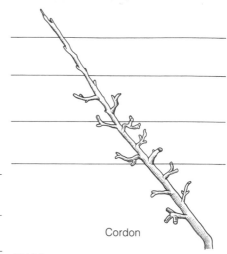

Cordon

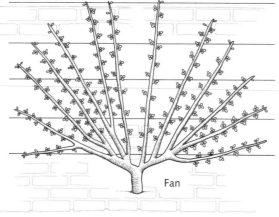

Fan

FAN

Another traditional method used widely for pears, peaches, plums and cherries. Again, they make very attractive wall plants and of course, take up very little space. Plant about 3.5m(12ft) apart.

SPINDLEBUSH

A popular method with commercial growers but not often used in gardens, though there's no reason why not. Instead of pruning, the branches are tied downwards to restrict the flow of sap and so induce heavy cropping early in the life of the tree. Plant about 2m(7ft) apart.

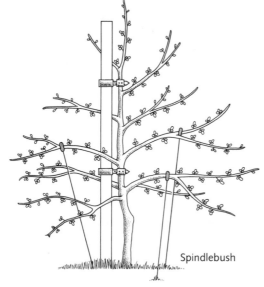

Spindlebush

Pollination

Apples

It's true to say that no variety of apple will produce a full crop unless it's pollinated by another variety. There is, in fact, a new selection of Cox's Orange Pippin from East Malling Research Station that is self-fertile but that one is, so far, unique.

Generally, apples that flower at the same time will pollinate each other, so choose at least two from the same flowering group. However, there are certain exceptions. Those varieties marked 'T' are triploids and won't pollinate anything. So, if you want to grow, say Bramley's Seedling, you'll have to choose two other varieties from the same group.

Some varieties are also biennial bearing and these are marked 'B'.

Flowering of apples

GROUP 1
Bolero
Gravenstein (T)
Lord Suffield
Mank's Codling (B)
Polka
Red Astrachan
Stark Earliest (syn. Scarlet Pimpernel)

GROUP 2
Acme
Adam's Pearmain (B)
Baker's Delicious
Beauty of Bath
Beauty of Blackmoor
Ben's Red (B)
Bismarck (B)
Cheddar Cross
Christmas Pearmain (B)
Devonshire Quarrenden (B)
Egremont Russet
George Cave
George Neal
Golden Spire
Idared
Irish Peach
Jerseymac
Kerry Pippin
Keswick Codling (B)
Laxton's Early Crimson
Lord Lambourne
Margil
McIntosh Red
Melba (B)
Merton Charm
Michaelmas Red
Norfolk Beauty
Owen Thomas
Rev. W. Wilks (B)
Ribston Pippin (T)
Ross Nonpareil
St Edmund's Pippin

Striped Beefing
Vista Bella (B)
Warner's King (T)
Washington (T)
White Transparent

GROUP 3
Acme
Allington Pippin (B)
Arthur Turner
Barnack Orange
Baumann's Reinette (B)
Belle de Boskoop (T)
Belle de Pontoise (B)
Blenheim Orange (TB)
Bountiful
Bowden's Seedling
Bramley's Seedling (T)
Brownlee's Russet
Charles Ross
Cox's Orange Pippin
Crispin (T)
Discovery
Duchess Favourite
Elstar
Emperor Alexander
Emneth Early
(Early Victoria) (B)
Encore
Epicure
Exeter Cross
Exquisite
Falstaff
Feltham Beauty
Fiesta
Fortuna (B)
Gavin
Goldilocks
Granny Smith
Greensleeves
Grenadier
Hambling's Seedling
Holstein (T)
Hormead Pearmain

James Grieve
John Standish
Jonagold (T)
Jonathan
Jupiter (T)
Karmijn de Sonnaville (T)
Katy (Katja)
Kent
Kidd's Orange Red
King of Tompkins County
King Russet
Lane's Prince Albert
Langley Pippin
Lord Derby
Lord Grosvenor
Lord Hindlip
Malling Kent
Mère de Ménage
Merton Knave
Merton Prolific
Merton Russet
Merton Worcester
Miller's Seedling (B)
Monarch
New Hawthornden
Newton Wonder
Norfolk Royal Russet
Ontario
Peasgood's Nonsuch
Queen
Red Charles Ross
Red Victoria (B)
Redsleeves
Reinette du Canada (T)
Rival (B)
Rosemary Russet
Rubinette
Shoesmith
St Cecilia
St Everard
Spartan
Stirling Castle
Sturmer Pippin
Sunset

Taunton Cross
Tom Putt
Tydeman's Early Worcester
Wagener (B)
Waltz
Wealthy
Worcester Pearmain
S.T. Wright
Wyken Pippin

GROUP 4
Annie Elizabeth
Ashmead's Kernel
Autumn Pearmain
Barnack Beauty
Bountiful
Chiver's Delight
Claygate Pearmain
Cornish Gillyflower
Cox's Pomona
D'Arcy Spice
Delicious
Duke of Devonshire
Dumelow's Seedling
   (Wellington)
Ellison's Orange
Elstar
Encore
Gala
George Carpenter
Gladstone (B)
Gloster 69
Golden Delicious
Golden Noble
Hawthornden
Herring's Pippin
Howgate Wonder
Ingrid Marie
Jester
Joybells
King's Acre Pippin
Lady Henniker
Lady Sudeley
Lanes Prince Albert

Laxton's Pearmain
Laxton's Superb (B)
Lord Derby
Mannington's Pearmain
Monarch (B)
Orleans Reinette
Pixie
Sir John Thornycroft
Tydeman's Late Orange
Winston
Woolbrook Russet
Yellow Newtown (B)

GROUP 5
Coronation (B)
Edward VII
Gascoyne's Scarlet (T)
King of the Pippins (B)
Merton Beauty
Mother (American)
Newton Wonder
Northern Spy (B)
Reinette Rouge Etoilée
Royal Jubilee
Suntan (T)
William Crump
Woolbrook Pippin (B)

GROUP 6
Bess Pool
Court Pendu Plat
Edward VII

GROUP 7
Crawley Beauty

Pears

Most pears need another variety for full pollination though Conference will set a reasonable crop on its own pollen but the fruits are rather misshapen and elongated. Again, simply choose two varieties from the same group. Here there are also triploids and some varieties that have sterile male flowers and are also useless as pollinators. They're marked 'MS'.

Key   T = triploid

MS = male sterile

Flowering of pears

GROUP 1
Brockworth Park
Maréchal de la Cour (T)
Précoce de Trévoux

GROUP 2
Baronne de Mello
Bellissime d'Hiver
Beurré Alexandre Lucas (T)
Beurré d'Amanlis (T)
Beurré d'Anjou
Beurré Clairgeau
Beurré Diel (T)
Beurré Giffard
Comtesse de Paris
Doyenne d'Eté
Duchesse d'Angoulême
Easter Beurré
Emile d'Heyst
Louise Bonne of Jersey
Marguerite Marillat (MS)
Packham's Triumph
Passe Crasanne
Princess
Seckle
St Luke
Uvedale's St Germain (T)
Vicar of Winkfield (T)

GROUP 3
Belle-Julie
Beurré Dumont
Beurré Hardy
Beurré Superfin
Black Worcester
Conference
Doyenne Boussoch (T)
Doyenne George Boucher
Dr Jules Guyot
Duchesse de Bordeaux
Durondeau
Fertility
Fondante d'Automne
Fondante Thirriott
Hessle
Jargonelle (T)
Josephine de Malines
Laxton's Early Market
Laxton's Progress
Laxton's Satisfaction
Le Lectier
Merton Pride (T)
Nouvelle Fulvie
Oliver de Serres
Roosevelt
Souvenir du Congrès
Thompson's
Triomphe de Vienne
Williams' Bon Chrétien

GROUP 4
Beth
Beurré Bedford (MS)
Beurré Mortillet
Bristol Cross (MS)
Calebasse Bosc
Catillac (T)

Clapp's Favourite
Concorde
Doyenne du Comice
Glou Morceau
Gorham
Improved Fertility
Laxton's Foremost
Laxton's Victor
Marie Louise
Napoleon
Nouveau Poiteau
Onward
Pitmaston Duchess (T)
Santa Claus
Winter Nelis
Zépherin Grégoire

The following pears are incompatible:
'Beurré d'Amanlis' with 'Conference'
and 'Doyenne du Comice' with
'Onward'. The following pears are all
incompatible with each other:
'Fondante d'Automne', 'Laxton's
Progress', 'Louise Bonne of Jersey',
'Précoce de Trévoux', 'Seckle', and
'Williams' Bon Chrétien'.
Triploid and male sterile pears are
ineffective as pollinators for others, so
two other pears are required, to
pollinate both themselves and the
triploid or male sterile cultivar.

Plums and Damsons

Plums are more complicated than
apples and pears. Some varieties are
self-fertile setting a full crop with their
own pollen. Others are partially self-
fertile and another group self-sterile.
Both these last two groups need a
pollinator which again must come from
the same flowering period or an
adjacent one.

It's all pretty complicated so to
simplify it, we've put the two groups of
varieties that need pollinating together
into five flowering periods.

Bear in mind though, that most of us
will only want one tree so a self-fertile
one is by far the best bet. Of course, it
doesn't matter when they flower unless
you want to use one to pollinate a
variety in one of the other groups.

Self-fertile plum varieties

GROUP 1
Monarch

GROUP 2
Avalon
Denniston's Superb
Reine-Claude de Bavay
Warwickshire Drooper

GROUP 3
Czar
Laxton's Cropper
Laxton's Supreme
Merryweather Damson
Opal
Pershore Yellow Egg
Purple Pershore
Thames Cross
Victoria

GROUP 4
Blaisdon Red
Bradley's King Damson
Early Transparent Gage
Giant Prune
Ontario
Oulin's Golden Gage

GROUP 5
Belle de Louvain
Marjorie's Seedling
Prune Damson

Cherries

Cherries are by far the most complicated and difficult to match. Many varieties, though flowering at the same time, will not pollinate certain other varieties. So, the only way to sort it out is to put all the incompatible varieties into a group. Then you know that in order to find a pollinator, you

Flowering of cherries

	Flowering period 1 (earliest)	Flowering period 2
Universal donors	Noir de Guben Nutberry Black	Merton Glory Merchant
Incompatibility group 1	Early Rivers	Bedford Prolific Knight's Early Black
Incompatibility group 2		Bigarreau de Schrecken Mermat Merton Favourite Waterloo
Incompatibility group 3		
Incompatibility group 4		
Incompatibility group 5		
Incompatibility group 6		Merton Heart
Incompatibility group 7		
Incompatibility group 8		
Incompatibility group 9		
Self-fertile		

need a variety which flowers at the same time yet comes from another group. So, for example, Early Amber will not pollinate Elton Heart or Governor Wood, but all of them will pollinate Merton Premier or Merton Marvel. Fortunately, there are now a few self-fertile varieties and any of these will pollinate all the others that flower at the same time.

Flowering period 3	Flowering period 4	Flowering period 5	Flowering period 6 (latest)
	Summit	Bigarreau Gaucher	
Frogmore Early Merton Bigarreau Merton Bounty Van	Belle Agathe Merton Crane		
Merton Marvel	Emperor Francis Napoleon Bigarreau		
Merton Premier	Kent Bigarreau		
		Late Black Bigarreau	
Early Amber Elton Heart Grosvenor Wood			
			Bradbourne Black Géante d'Hedelfinger
Peggy Rivers			
	Merton Reward	Merton Late	
Lapins May Duke	Stella Sunburst	Morello	

Rootstocks

Most fruit trees are grafted or budded onto a rootstock. You can see the join about 30cm(1ft) above the ground where there's a small kink in the stem.

The rootstocks which were developed at government research stations, have the effect of controlling the growth and eventual size of the tree. They also have a marked effect on the time taken for the tree to come into regular fruiting. Dwarfing roostock bring trees into bearing within the second or third year.

If you want a very large tree or your soil is particularly poor, choose a vigorous stock but remember that it will take longer to crop.

If your soil is good and you want a very small tree, choose a very dwarfing stock, while on poor soil a semi-dwarfing one will be best. Remember too that trees on dwarfing stocks will need staking all their lives.

On the good soil at Barnsdale, the larger, bush apple trees are on MM106 stocks while the cordons and espaliers are on M9. These are certainly the two most common stocks found in nurseries and garden centres. There are also some trees in containers and they are on M27 and doing well but they need constant attention to watering and feeding.

All the pears at Barnsdale are on Quince A and the plums, peaches, nectarines, etc, are on Pixy. I would recommend this for all but the very poorest soil.

Cherries are generally budded onto Colt stocks, but bear in mind that they still make big trees. At Barnsdale I compromize by growing them as fans and keeping them smaller by pruning.

Bear in mind that the sizes quoted here are approximate, since growth is also affected by soil and climate. If in doubt, ask the stockist and if they can't tell you the rootstock as well as the variety, go elsewhere.

Apples

MM111

Very vigorous, but good for poor soils. Can be used for standards and half standards, espaliers and fans. Height and spread is 20ft (5.5m), yields from 4–5cwt (200–250kg), crops 5–6 years after planting. Ideal if you want to plant a traditional orchard.

MM106

Semi-dwarfing, for half standards, large bushes, fans, espaliers and cordons on poor soil. Height and spread is 15ft, yields around 1 cwt, crops after 3–5 years.

M26

Dwarfing for bushes, cordons and small espaliers. Height and spread is 12ft, yields around 75lbs, crops after 3 years.

M9

Very dwarfing rootstock, for bushes and cordons. Needs good soil and permanent staking. Height and spread is 10ft (3m), yields around 40lbs (18kg), crops after 2–3 years.

M27

Extremely dwarfing, for cordons and growing in containers. Needs careful watering and feeding, and some permanent support. Height and spread is 6ft (1.8m), yields around 20lbs (9kg), crops after 2 years.

Pears and some medlars

QUINCE A

Fairly vigorous, common stock, for all garden forms. Height and spread 15ft (4.6m), yields 100lbs (45.36kg), crops after 4 years.

QUINCE C

Semi-dwarfing, used for strong growing types, needs fertile soil. Height and spread 12ft (3.6m), yields 75lbs (34kg), crops after 3 years.

Plums, damsons, gages, peaches, nectarines and apricots

ST JULIAN A

Fairly vigorous, best for large gardens or poor soils. Height and spread 15ft (4.6m), yields 50lbs (22.68kg), crops after 2 years.

PIXY dwarf

Good for heavy soils. Height and spread 8ft (2.4m), yields 20lbs (9kg), crops after 2 years.

Cherries

COLT

Semi-dwarfing, for most soils. Height and spread 15ft (4.6m), yields 20lbs (9kg), crops after 3 years.

INMIL Dwarf
Needs good soil and permanent stakes.
Height and spread 12ft (3.6m), yield
15lbs (6.8kg), crops after 3 years.

Mulberries

These are grown on their own roots
and generally propagated by cuttings.

Figs

Also grown on their own roots from
cutings or layers.

Quinces

QUINCE A
A rootstock of medium vigour for most
soils.

QUINCE C
Slightly dwarfer for really good soils.

General Chart Showing Cropping Periods of Fruit

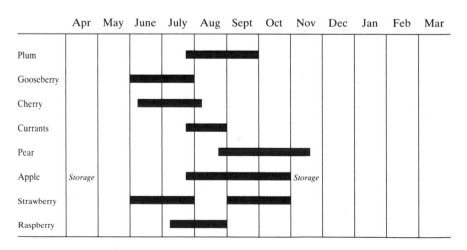

	Apr	May	June	July	Aug	Sept	Oct	Nov	Dec	Jan	Feb	Mar
Plum				███	███	██						
Gooseberry		███	██									
Cherry		███	███									
Currants				███	██							
Pear						███	███					
Apple	*Storage*			███	███	███	███	*Storage*				
Strawberry		███	███			███	███					
Raspberry			███	███								

Vegetables and Herbs

The following tables are designed to help new vegetable and herb gardeners grow a succession of crops. Old hands will have their own favourite varieties, but I would suggest that even they try something new each year. There have been some excellent developments lately that have made many older varieties obsolete.

The sowing dates are deliberately rather vague since they'll vary somewhat in different parts of the country. However, absolute accuracy is unnecessary, though you should bear in mind that no vegetable seeds will germinate at temperatures much below about 7C(45F). So for the first sowings in early spring it's better to err on the late side.

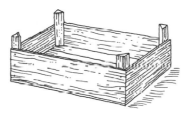

To grow a succession of vegetables

Vegetable	Barnsdale recommended varieties	Gromore or pelleted chicken manure	Sow in greenhouse
Artichoke (Globe)	'Green Globe'	4oz per sq.yd 136g per sq.m	Late Jan–Feb
Artichoke (Jerusalem)	'Fuseau'	4oz per sq.yd 136g per sq.m	
Asparagus	'Sorbonne'	4oz per sq. yd 136g per sq.m	Feb
Aubergine	'Black Prince'	Weekly liquid feeds	Feb–March
Beans Broad	'Aquadulce' 'Jubilee Hysor' 'The Sutton' (dwarf)	3oz per sq.yd 102g per sq.m	Feb
French	'Daisy' 'Limelight' 'Purple podded' 'Tendergreen'	4½oz per sq.yd 153g per sq.m	March/April April
Runner	'Mergoles' 'Painted Lady' 'Pickwick' 'Polestar'	2oz per sq.yd 68g per sq.m	April
Beetroot	'Boltardy' 'Burpees Golden' 'Cylindra' 'Early wonder'	8oz per sq.yd 272g per sq.m in 2 applications	Feb
Broccoli & Calabrese	'Early Purple' 'Green Comet' 'Mercedes' 'Romanesco' 'White sprouting'	4½oz per sq.yd 153g per sq.m	
Brussels sprouts	'Fortress' 'Peer Gynt' 'Widgeon'	10oz per sq.yd 340g per sq.m in 2 applications	

Sow under cloche	Sow outdoors	Spacing between plants	Spacing between rows	Harvest
	March	As annual: 45cm (18in)	90cm (36in)	July/Aug
		As perennial: 90cm (3ft)	90cm (36in)	
	early spring	30cm (1ft)		In winter as required
		Plant crowns 30cm (1ft) in June		May/June from 3rd year
		9in (23cm)	pots under glass	August onwards while shiny
Jan/Feb	Nov or Feb March/April	10cm (4in)	30cm(12in)	June onwards
March/ April	April–July in succession April June	20cm (8in)	30cm (12in)	July onwards
April	mid May	30cm (12in)	60cm (24in)	Late July onwards
		(no support needed)		
March	April–July	8cm (3in)	30cm (12in)	June–Oct to store
	May	60cm (24in)	30cm (12in)	Jan onwards
	April	15cm (6in)	30cm (12in)	July onwards

Vegetable	Barnsdale recommended varieties	Gromore or pelleted chicken manure	Sow in greenhouse
Cabbage Spring	'April' 'Offenham' 'Durham Early'	8oz per sq.yd 272g per sq.m in 2 applications	
Summer	'Kingspi' 'Primo'	10oz per sq.yd 340g per sq.m in 2 applications	Feb
Autumn	'Castello' 'Celtic'	10oz per sq.yd 340g per sq.m in 2 applications	
Winter	'Celtic' 'January King'	As above	
Calabrese (see Cauliflower)			
Capsicum (see Peppers)			
Carrot	'Autumn King' 'Early Nantes' 'Rondo'	1oz per sq.yd 34g per sq.m	Late Jan
Cauliflower Summer	'Alpha'	8oz per sq.yd 272g per sq.m	Jan–Feb
Autumn	'Dok Elgon'	4½oz per sq.yd 153g per sq.m	
Winter	'Purple Cape' 'Newton Seale' 'Walcheren Winter'	as above	
Celeriac	'Snow White'	4oz per sq.yd 136g per sq.m	Feb/March
Celery	'Celebrity' 'Giant Pink'	4oz per sq.yd 136g per sq.m	Feb/March

Sow under cloche	Sow outdoors	Spacing between plants	Spacing between rows	Harvest
	March–April	15cm (6in)	space out to 1m (3ft) square	Oct onwards Dec onwards
	July–Aug	Transplant seedlings 45cm (18in) sq. in Sept/Oct		March onwards
	April	as above in June		July onwards
	April/May	Transplant seedlings 45cm (18in) sq. in July		Oct onwards
Feb		Multiple sowing 8cm (3in)	30cm (12in)	As required As required
	March–July monthly			Nov to store
	April onwards 3 week intervals	60cm (24in) sq.		Develop as curds
	April April–May	75cm (30in) sq.		Aug/Sep As required
		30cm (1ft)	35cm (15in)	autumn
	April	in blocks 23cm (9in) sq. 30cm (12in)	In trenches 45cm (18in)	before frost As required
	May	23cm (9in)	30cm (12in)	Dig up in autumn for blanching

Vegetable	Barnsdale recommended varieties	Gromore or pelleted chicken manure	Sow in greenhouse
Chicory Blanched chicons: Unblanched:	'Apollo' 'Normanto' 'Crystal heart' 'Sugar Loaf'	4oz per sq.yd 136g per sq.m as above	
Courgette and Marrow	'Ambassador' 'Gold Rush' 'Long Green Striped'	4oz per sq.yd 136g per sq.m	April
Cucumber	'Athene' (G/H) 'Bush Champion' 'Long Green'	4oz per sq.yd 136g per sq.m + weekly liquid feed 4oz per sq.yd 136g per sq.m	April–May
Endive	'Moss curled' 'Batavian Broad Leaved'	2oz per sq.yd 68g per sq.m	
Florence Fennel	'Cantino'	4oz per sq.yd 136g per sq.m	
Garlic	'Long Keeper'	4oz per sq.yd 136g per sq.m	
Hamburg Parsley (*see* Parsnip)			
Kale	'Hungry Gap' 'Pentland Brig'	4oz per sq.yd 136g per sq.m	
Kohl Rabi	'Rowel'	4oz per sq.yd 136g per sq.m	
Land cress	–	4oz per sq.yd 136g per sq.m	
Leek	'Musselburgh' 'St. Victor'	5oz per sq.yd 170g per sq.m	Late March

Sow under cloche	Sow outdoors	Spacing between plants	Spacing between rows	Harvest
	June/July	25cm (10in)	25cm (10in)	When hearted Oct onwards
April	End May	60cm (24in) square		at 15cm (6in) at 35cm (15in)
	End May	Singly in pots in g/house Up canes or wigwams 60cm (2ft) apart 90cm (36in) sq.		June onwards at regular intervals
	May/June Aug	thin to 30cm (12in)	30cm (12in)	Aug/Sept 3 weeks after blanching
	In succession May–Aug July	Thin to 20cm (8in)	45cm (18in)	Aug onwards Oct/Nov
	Plant cloves Oct		15cm (6in) sq.	July/Aug
	April		45cm (18in)	Leaves from centre of plant during winter
March	April–July in succession	23cm (9in)	30cm (12in)	after 10–12 weeks 2–3in diam.
	March–Aug	15cm (6in)	30cm (12in)	after 8–10 weeks
	April	15cm (6in) 30cm (12in) sq. if multiple sown	30cm (12in)	in winter as required

Vegetable	Barnsdale recommended varieties	Gromore or pelleted chicken manure	Sow in greenhouse
Lettuce	'Kellys' 'Little Gem' 'Lollo Rosso' 'Salad Bowl' 'Saladin' 'Sigmaball' 'Tom Thumb'	4oz per sq.yd 136g per sq.m	Sept–Jan Late Jan
Marrow (*see* courgette)			
Melon	'Ogen' 'Sweetheart'	4oz per sq.yd 136g per sq.m + weekly liquid feed	April
Onions	'Albion' 'Brunswick' 'Express Yellow' 'Hygro' 'Rijnsburger' 'Unwins First Early'	4oz per sq.yd 136g per sq.m 8oz per sq.yd 272g per sq.m in 2 applications 4oz per sq.yd 136g per sq.m	Jan–Feb
Salad onions/Spring onions	'White Lisbon'	3oz per sq.yd 102g per sq.m	Jan–Feb
Parsnips/Hamburg Parsley	'Tender & True' White Gem'	3oz per sq.yd 102g per sq.m	
Peas	'Cavalier' 'Douce Provence' 'Onward' 'Oregon Sugar Pod'	None needed	Feb
Peppers Sweet Hot	'Early Prolific' 'Gypsy' 'Redskin' 'Hot Mexican'	Weekly liquid feed	Jan
Potato	'Concorde' 'Foremost' 'Cara' 'Pink Fir Apple' 'Romano'	5oz per sq.yd 170g per sq.m 8oz per sq.yd 272g per sq.m in 2 applications	

Sow under cloche	Sow outdoors	Spacing between plants	Spacing between rows	Harvest
late Feb		15cm (6in)	30cm (12in)	when hearted
	April–July fortnightly in succession	23cm (9in)	30cm (12in)	Pull leaves as required Dec–April
		In frames or greenhouse in 23cm (9in) pots or growing bags, 2 plants per bag or 60cm apart in the border		
	March (or plant sets)	7.5cm (3in)	30cm (12in)	Aug/Sept to store
	Aug Plant sets Oct			July Aug/Sept June
Feb	March–July monthly	sow thinly	8cm (3in)	June–Sept
	March/April	15cm (6in)	30cm (12in)	December after frost
Feb	March April + May fortnightly March–June	5cm (2in)	45cm (18in)	regularly while young
		60cm (24in) or 20cm (8in) pots	60cm (24in)	green or red green or red red green or red
	March	30cm (12in)	30cm (12in)	as required when in flower May–June to store

Vegetable	Barnsdale recommended varieties	Gromore or pelleted chicken manure	Sow in greenhouse
Pumpkin	'Hubbard Golden Squash' 'Table Ace' 'Veg. spaghetti'	8oz per sq.yd 272g per sq.m in 2 applications	April
Radish	'Cherry Belle' 'French Breakfast'	1 oz per sq.yd 34g per sq.m	Jan
Ruby Chard (see Swiss Chard)			
Salsify	'Mammoth'	4oz per sq.yd 136g per sq.m	
Scorzonera	'Habil'	4oz per sq.yd 136g per sq.m	
Silver Beet/Sea Kale Beet (*see* Swiss Chard)			
Shallots (sets)	'Dutch Red' 'Dutch Yellow'	5oz per sq.yd 170g per sq.m	
Spinach	'Bloomsdale' 'Melody' 'Symphony'	8oz per sq.yd 272g per sq.m in 2 applications	Feb
Spinach Beet	'Perpetual'	4oz per sq.yd 136g per sq.m	
Swede	'Marian' 'Purple Top Yellow'	3oz per sq.yd 102g per sq.m	
Sweetcorn	'Early Xtra Sweet'		April
Swiss Chard (also called Silver Kale and Sea Kale)	'Fordhook Giant' 'Ruby Chard'	4oz per sq.yd 136g per sq.m	
Tomato (outdoor) Bush (upright)	'Red Alert' 'Tornado' 'Outdoor Girl' 'Yellow Perfection'	8oz per sq.yd 272g per sq.m in 2 applications	

Sow under cloche	Sow outdoors	Spacing between plants	Spacing between rows	Harvest
	March	35cm (15in)	75cm (30in)	Oct
	mid May	90cm (36in) sq		When skin is hard
	March–Sept fortnightly	thinly	15cm (6in)	as required
	April	15cm (6in)	30cm (12in)	Oct–Nov
	April	15cm (6in)	30cm (12in)	Oct–Nov
	Feb–March	15cm (6in)	30cm (12in)	June onwards
March	March July monthly	15cm (6in)	30cm (12in)	May–Nov Pick a few leaves reg. from plant
	April August then cover with cloches	30cm (12in)	30cm (12in)	July/Aug March/April
	May/June	30cm (12in)	45cm (18in)	Oct onwards Nov to store
April		60cm (24in) sq. in a block		when tassels are black
	April July	30cm (12in)	35cm (15in)	July/Aug winter as req. A few leaves from each plant
		60cm (24in) 60cm (24in)	outdoors 90cm (3ft)	Pick reg.

Vegetable	Barnsdale recommended varieties	Gromore or pelleted chicken manure	Sow in greenhouse
Tomato (indoor)	'Ailsa Craig' 'Gardeners Delight' 'Shirley' 'Sungold'	Twice weekly liquid feed	Feb
Turnips	'Early Milan' 'Golden Ball' 'Purple Top'	4½oz per sq.yd 153g per sq.m	Jan

To grow a succession of herbs

Common name	Botanical name	Annual/Biennial Perennial	Propagation
Anise	*Pimpinella anisum*	Half hardy annual	Sow in spring
Angelica	*Angelica archangelica*	Hardy herbaceous biennial	Sow in autumn
Sweet Basil	*Ocimum basilicum*	Tender annual	Sow indoors in heat, late spring
Bay	*Laurus nobilis*	Evergreen tree	Take stem cuttings or layer in late summer
Bergamot	*Monarda didyma*	Hardy herbaceous perennial	Divide or take root cuttings in spring
Borage	*Borago officinalis*	Hardy annual	Sow in spring
Caraway	*Carum carvi*	Hardy annual	Sow late spring or early autumn
Chamomile	*Chamaemelum nobile*	Hardy evergreen perennial	Take cuttings in summer; divide in spring or summer
Chervil	*Anthriscus cerefolium*	Hardy annual	Sow monthly in summer

Sow under cloche	Sow outdoors	Spacing between plants	Spacing between rows	Harvest
		Growing bags (3 per bag) 23cm (9in) pots 45cm (18in) apart in borders		Regularly as they ripen
Feb	May–July	30cm (6in)	30cm (12in)	as required golf-tennis ball size Nov to store

Growing Position	Height	Uses: Aromatic/ Culinary/Medicinal
Well drained, alkaline soil Sunny, sheltered position	18in 45cm	whole plant: c seed: a+m+c
Moist soil Light shade	3–8ft 1–2.5m	leaf: m leaf seed root: a leaf & stem: c+m
Moist, well drained soil Sunny, sheltered position	18in 45cm	leaf: c+m
Rich, well drained, moist soil. Full sun, sheltered position	23ft 7m	leaf: m+a+c
Rich, light, moist soil Sunny position	2–3ft 60cm–1m	leaf: m+c+a
Well drained soil Sunny position	1–2ft 6in 30–75cm	leaf & seed: m flower & leaf: c
Well drained soil Sun	2ft 60cm	root & seed: c seed: m
Well drained soil Full sun	8in 20cm	flower: m+a
Well drained soil Light shade	10–15in 25–38cm	leaf: c+m

Common name	Botanical name	Annual/Biennial Perennial	Propagation
Chicory	*Cichorium intybus*	Hardy perennial	Sow early summer
Chives	*Allium schoenoprasum*	Hardy perennial	Take offsets or divide bulb in autumn or spring
Chinese chives (or Garlic chives)	*Allium tuberosum*	Hardy perennial	Take offsets or divide bulb in autumn or spring
Comfrey	*Symphytum officinale*	Hardy herbaceous perennial	Take root offsets spring, summer or autumn
Coriander	*Coriandrum sativum*	Hardy annual	Sow in autumn or spring
Cotton lavender	*Santolina chamaecyparissus*	Perennial	Stem cuttings in spring or from midsummer to autumn
Dill	*Anethum graveolens*	Hardy annual	Sow in spring
English mace	*Achillea decolorans*	Half hardy perennial	Sow in spring
Everlasting onion	*Allium cepa*	Hardy perennial	Divide in autumn or spring
Fennel	*Foeniculum vulgare*	Hardy herbaceous perennial	Sow in late spring, divide in autumn
Garlic	*Allium sativum*	Hardy perennial	Plant cloves in autumn Sow seed in spring
Horseradish	*Armoracia rusticana*	Hardy perennial	Sow or divide roots in spring
Hyssop	*Hyssopus officinalis*	Hardy semi-evergreen shrub	Stem cuttings in summer
Lavender	*Lavandula angustifolia*	Hardy evergreen shrub	Stem cuttings in autumn or spring—divide or layer

Growing Position	Height	Uses: Aromatic/ Culinary/Medicinal
Light soil Sunny position	3–5ft 1–1.5m	leaf & root: m chicon & root: c
Rich, well drained soil Sunny position	8–12in 20–30cm	leaf: c+m whole plant: m
Rich, well drained soil Sunny position	8–12in 20–30cm	leaf & flower: c whole plant: m
Soil rich in nitrogen Full sun	3–4ft 1–1.2m	leaf: c+m
Rich, light soil Full sun	2ft 60cm	leaf: c seed: a+c+m
Well drained soil Sun	2ft 60cm	leaf: a flower & leaf: m
Rich, well drained soil Sunny, sheltered position	2–5ft 60cm–1.5m	seed & leaf: c seed: m
Sandy soil	18in 45cm	leaf: a
Rich, moist soil Sunny position		bulb: c
Well drained soil Full sun	7ft 2.1m	seed, leaf & bulb: c seed: m
Rich, well drained soil Sunny position	12in 30cm	bulb: c+m
Rich, moist soil Sunny position	2–3ft 60cm–1m	root: m+c leaf: c
Well drained alkaline soil Full sun	18in–4ft 45cm–1.2m	leaf & flower: a+c+m
Well drained Sunny, open position	18in–3ft 45cm–1m	flower: a+c+m

Common name	Botanical name	Annual/Biennial Perennial	Propagation
Lemon balm	*Melissa officinalis*	Hardy herbaceous perennial	Sow in spring Divide spring or autumn
Lemon verbena	*Aloysia triphylla*	Half hardy shrub	Sow in spring Softwood cuttings late spring
Lovage	*Levisticum officinale*	Hardy herbaceous perennial	Sow late summer. Root cuttings in spring or autumn
Marjoram	*Origanum marjorana*	Half hardy herbaceous perennial	Sow in spring
Mints Applemint	*Mentha suaveolens*	Hardy herbaceous perennial	Root or stem cuttings or divide in spring or autumn
Variegated Applemint	*Mentha suaveolens* 'Variegata'	Hardy herbaceous perennial	Root or stem cuttings or divide in spring or autumn
Corsican mint	*Mentha requienii*	Hardy herbaceous perennial	Root or stem cuttings or divide in spring or autumn
Creeping Pennyroyal	*Mentha pulegium*	Hardy herbaceous perennial	Root or stem cuttings or divide in spring or autumn
Curly mint	*Mentha spicata* 'Crispa'	Hardy herbaceous perennial	Root or stem cuttings or divide in spring or autumn
Eau de Cologne mint	*Mentha × piperita* 'Citrata'	Hardy herbaceous perennial	Root or stem cuttings or divide in spring or autumn
Gingermint	*Mentha × gentilis* 'Variegata'	Hardy herbaceous perennial	Root or stem cuttings or divide in spring or autumn
Lemon mint	*Mentha × piperita* 'Citrata Lemon'	Hardy herbaceous perennial	Root or stem cuttings or divide in spring or autumn
Moroccan spearmint	*Mentha spicata* 'Moroccan'	Hardy herbaceous perennial	Root or stem cuttings or divide in spring or autumn

Growing Position	Height	Uses: Aromatic/ Culinary/Medicinal
Moist soil Sunny position	3ft 1m	leaf: a+c+m
Light, well drained alkaline soil. Full sun, sheltered position	2–4ft 60cm–1.2m	leaf: a+c+m
Rich, moist, well drained soil. Sunny position or partial shade	7ft 2.1m	seed & leaf: c+m
Well drained, rich, alkaline soil. Full sun	2ft 60cm	flower: m leaf: c+a
Rich, moist, well drained alkaline soil. Sun or partial shade	2ft 60cm	leaf: a+c
Rich, moist, well drained alkaline soil. Sun or partial shade	2ft 60cm	leaf: a+c
Rich, moist, well drained alkaline soil. Sun or partial shade	1in 2.5cm	leaf: a+c+m
Rich, moist, well drained alkaline soil. Sun or partial shade	6 in 15cm	leaf: a+m
Rich, moist, well drained alkaline soil. Sun or partial shade	16in 40cm	leaf: a+c
Rich, moist, well drained alkaline soil. Sun or partial shade	18in 45cm	leaf: a
Rich, moist, well drained alkaline soil. Sun or partial shade	16in 40cm	leaf: a+c
Rich, moist, well drained alkaline soil. Sun or partial shade	16in 40cm	leaf: a+c
Rich, moist, well drained alkaline soil. Sun or partial shade	2ft 60cm	leaf: a+c+m

Common name	Botanical name	Annual/Biennial Perennial	Propagation
Peppermint	Mentha × piperita	Hardy herbaceous perennial	Root or stem cuttings or divide in spring or autumn
Red raripila spearmint	Mentha rubra raripila	Hardy herbaceous perennial	Root or stem cuttings or divide in spring or autumn
Upright Pennyroyal	Mentha pulegium 'Upright'	Hardy herbaceous perennial	Root or stem cuttings or divide in spring or autumn
Mustard	Sinapis alba	Hardy annual	Sow in spring for seed or every 3 weeks for salad
Nasturtium	Tropaeolum majus	Hardy annual	Sow late spring
Tree onion (or Egyptian Onion)	Allium cepa proliferum	Hardy perennial	Divide bulb in autumn or spring
Welsh onion	Allium fistulosum	Hardy perennial	Divide bulb in autumn or spring
Oregano (Wild marjoram)	Origanum vulgare	Hardy herbaceous perennial	Sow in spring Divide, take stem or root cuttings
Golden marjoram	Origanum vulgare 'Aureum'	Hardy herbaceous perennial	Sow in spring Divide, take stem or root cuttings
Parsley	Petroselinum crispum	Hardy biennial	Sow spring–summer
Pot marigold	Calendula officinalis	Hardy annual	Sow seed in spring in situ or singly in pots
Pot marjoram	Origanum onites	Perennial	Sow in spring. Divide spring or autumn. Take root or stem cuttings late spring to midsummer
Purslane	Portulaca oleracea	Half hardy	Sow monthly during summer

Growing Position	Height	Uses: Aromatic/ Culinary/Medicinal
Rich, moist, well drained alkaline soil. Sun or partial shade	2.5ft 75cm	leaf: a+c+m
Rich, moist, well drained alkaline soil. Sun or partial shade	2ft 60cm	leaf: a+c+m
Rich, moist, well drained alkaline soil. Sun or partial shade	12in 30cm	leaf: a
Fertile, well drained soil Sunny position	1–8ft 30cm–2.4m	seed & leaf: c seed: m
Well drained soil Full sun or partial shade	1–2ft 30–60cm	leaf & flower & seed: c
Rich, moist, well drained soil	3ft 1m	bulb: c
Rich, moist, well drained soil	12in 30cm	leaf: c
Rich, well drained, alkaline soil. Full sun	2ft 60cm	leaf: c+m
Rich, well drained, alkaline soil. Full sun	2ft 60cm	leaf: c+m
Rich, moist soil Full sun or light shade	15in 38cm	leaf. c+m
All soils Full sun	1–2ft 30–60cm	flower: c+m
Well drained, alkaline soil	6in–2ft 15–60cm	stem: c leaf: a+c+m flowering top: m
Well drained soil Sunny, sheltered position	6in 15cm	leaf & stem: c+m

Common name	Botanical name	Annual/Biennial Perennial	Propagation
Rosemary	*Rosmarinus officinalis*	Hardy evergreen perennial	Sow in heat in spring or take cuttings or layers
Rue	*Ruta graveolens*	Hardy evergreen sub-shrub	Divide in spring. Take stem cuttings late summer. Sow in spring
Sage	*Salvia officinalis*	Hardy evergreen shrub	Sow seed in spring. Take cuttings in summer
Scented Geranium Apple scent	*Pelargonium odoratissimum*	Tender evergreen perennial	Take cuttings in summer. Grow in pots
Incense	*P. quercifolium*	Tender evergreen perennial	Take cuttings in summer. Grow in pots
Orange	*P. crispum* 'Prince of Orange'	Tender evergreen perennial	Take cuttings in summer. Grow in pots
Nutmeg	*P. × fragrans*	Tender evergreen perennial	Take cuttings in summer. Grow in pots
Rose	*P. capitatum*	Tender evergreen perennial	Take cuttings in summer. Grow in pots
Rose-lemon	*P. radens*	Tender evergreen perennial	Take cuttings in summer. Grow in pots
Peppermint	*P. graveolens* 'Lady Plymouth'	Tender evergreen perennial	Take cuttings in summer. Grow in pots
Sorrel	*Rumex rugosus* *Rumex scutatus*	Hardy perennial	Sow in spring or divide in autumn
Sweet cicely	*Myrrhis odorata*	Hardy herbaceous perennial	Sow outdoors in autumn

Growing Position	Height	Uses: Aromatic/ Culinary/Medicinal
Well drained soil Sunny, sheltered position	3–6ft 1–2m	leaf: c+m flower & leaf: a+c leaf: m
Well drained, alkaline soil Full sun	2ft 60cm	leaf: m seed & leaf: c
Light, well drained alkaline soil Full sun	1–2ft 6in 30–75cm	leaf: c+m flower: c
Well drained compost Sunny position	1–3ft 30cm–1m	leaf: a+c+m flower: c
Well drained compost Sunny position	1–3ft 30cm–1m	leaf: a+c+m flower: c
Well drained compost Sunny position	1–3ft 30cm–1m	leaf: a+c+m flower: c
Well drained compost Sunny position	1–3ft 30cm–1m	leaf: a+c+m flower: c
Well drained compost Sunny position	1–3ft 30cm–1m	leaf: a+c+m flower: c
Well drained compost Sunny position	1–3ft 30cm–1m	leaf: a+c+m flower: c
Well drained compost Sunny position	1–3ft 30cm–1m	leaf: a+c+m flower: c
Moist, sunny site. Well drained Full sun. Sheltered position	2–4ft 60cm–1.2m	leaf: c+m
Rich soil Light shade	3ft 1m	seed & leaf: c leaf: m

Common name	Botanical name	Annual/Biennial Perennial	Propagation
Sweet Rocket	*Hesperis matronalis*	Hardy biennial	Sow outdoors in late spring
Southernwood	*Artemesia abrotanum*	Perennial	Sow when available Take semi-hardwood cuttings late summer
Tansy	*Tanacetum vulgare*	Perennial	Sow in spring. Divide roots in spring or autumn
French Tarragon	*Artemisia dracunculus*	Hardy perennial	Divide roots in spring. Take stem cuttings in summer
Common Thyme	*Thymus vulgaris*	Evergreen shrub	Divide, layer or take cuttings in spring, summer or autumn
Wild Thyme	*T. praecox arcticus*	Evergreen shrub	Divide, layer or take cuttings in spring, summer or autumn
Lemon-scented Thyme	*T. citriodorus*	Evergreen shrub	Divide, layer or take cuttings in spring, summer or autumn
Golden Lemon-scented Thyme	*T. citriodorous* 'Aureus'	Evergreen shrub	Divide, layer or take cuttings in spring, summer or autumn
Winter Savory	*Satureja montana*	Hardy evergreen shrub	Sow or divide in spring or autumn

Growing Position	Height	Uses: Aromatic/ Culinary/Medicinal
Rich loam Full sun or light shade	3ft 1m	flower: a+c leaf: c
Light soils Full sun	2–4ft 60cm–1.2m	leaf: c+m
Any soil that is not too wet Full sun or light shade	2–5ft 60cm–1m	flower & leaf: m leaf: c
Rich, light soil Sunny, sheltered position	2–3ft 60cm–1m	leaf: c+m
Light, well drained soil Full sun	12in 30cm	leaf: a+c+m
Light, well drained soil Full sun	4in 10cm	leaf: a+c+m
Light, well drained soil Full sun	6in 15cm	leaf: a+c+m
Light, well drained soil Full sun	6in 15cm	leaf: a+c+m
Well drained, alkaline soil Full sun.	15in 38cm	leaf: c+m flower: m

Germination

The following list of germination times and temperatures is, of course, somewhat approximate.

All of them refer to seedlings raised in the greenhouse and, where vegetables are mentioned, these too refer to early crops sown under glass for either growing on in the greenhouse, or for planting out under cloches.

Where seeds need light to germinate, they should be covered with a thin layer of horticultural vermiculite and then with either a sheet of glass or clear polythene.

When the seeds need darkness they can be covered with a thin layer of compost or not at all and then with opaque polythene or kitchen foil.

Those that remain unmarked are not too fussy so it's recommended to cover them with a little vermiculite and then with opaque polythene.

Germination times for seeds sown outside vary so much that there's little point in listing them. But you should be able to get an approximation from this chart used in conjunction with the prevailing weather conditions and soil temperature.

Seeds – Germination

Variety	Germination Days	Light/ Dark	Temperature (°F)
Achillea	21–30	L	60–65
Achimenes	21–30		65–75
Adonis	30–120		60–65
Ageratum	10–14	L	70–75
Alstroemeria	30–365		65–70
Alyssum	7–14	L	55–75
Amaranthus	10–15		70–75
Amaryllis	21–70		65–75
Anchusa	7–30		65–70
Anemone	28–180		65–70
Aquilegia	30–90	L	65–75
Arabis	20–25	L	65–70

Variety	Germination Days	Light/ Dark	Temperature (°F)
Arctotis	21–35		60–70
Arenaria	15–30		55–65
Armeria	14–21		55–60
Artichoke	7–8		65–70
Asparagus	21–30		60–70
Asperula	30–42	L	50–55
Aster	10–14		65–70
Astilbe	40–80		60–65
Atriplex	9–21		50–55
Aubergine	6–7		65–70
Aubrieta	14–21	L	60–65
Basil	7–10		60–70
Beetroot	7–8		60–65
Begonia	15–60	L	70–80
Bellis	10–15	L	60–70
Broad Beans	7–8		60–65
Browallia	14–21	L	70–75
Cabbage	2–3		55–60
Cacti	5–180	L	75–80
Calandrinia	5–14		55–60
Calceolaria	14–21	L	65–75
Calendula	10–14	D	65–70
Campanula	14–28	L	60–70
Candytuft	10–15		68–85
Canna	21–60		70–75
Capsicum	21–30	L	70–75
Carrot	6–7		55–60
Catananche	21–25		65–75
Cauliflower	2–3		55–60
Celery	10–11	L	65–70
Celosia	10–15	L	70–75
Centaurea	7–14	D	60–70
Centranthus	21–30		60–70
Cerastium	5–10		55–60
Cheiranthus	14–21		65–75
Chelone	14–42		55–65
Chrysanthemum	10–18		60–70
Cineraria	14–21	L	65–70
Clarkia	21		50–55
Cleome	10–14	L	70–75
Cobaea	21–30		70–75
Coleus	10–20	L	65–75

Variety	Germination Days	Light/ Dark	Temperature (°F)
Convolvulus	5–14		65–70
Coreopsis	20–25	L	55–70
Corydalis	30–60	L	50–60
Courgette	7		65–70
Craspedia	14–30		70–75
Cucumber	7		70–75
Cuphea	8–10	L	65–70
Cyclamen	30–60	D	55–60
Cynoglossum	5–10	D	65–75
Cyperus	25–30		70–75
Dahlia	5–20		65–70
Delphinium	14–28	D	50–55
Dianthus	14–21		60–70
Digitalis	15–20	L	60–65
Dimorphotheca	10–15	L	60–70
Eccremocarpus	30–60		55–60
Echinops	15–60		60–65
Echium	7–14		65–70
Erigeron	15–20		55–60
Eschscholtzia	14–21		60–65
Eucalyptus	14–90		70–75*
Euphorbia	10–15		65–70
Exacum	15–20	L	70–75
Ferns	30–180	L	65–70
Ficus	15–90	L	70–80
Freesia	25–30		65–75
Fuchsia	21–90	L	70–75
Gaillardia	15–20	L	65–70
Gaura	14–30		65–75
Gazania	8–21	D	60–65
Gentiana	14–180	D	70–75
Geranium	3–21		70–75
Gerbera	15–25	L	70–75
Gesneria	14–21	L	70–75
Geum	21–28+		65–70
Gilia	17		
Gloxinia	15–30	L	65–75
Godetia	7–14		60–65
Gourds	15–28		70–75
Grasses	10–90	L	60–75
Grevillea	20–25	L	75–80
Gypsophila	10–15		65–70

Variety	Germination Days	Light/ Dark	Temperature (°F)
Helianthus	10–14		65–70
Helichrysum	7–10	L	65–75
Helleborus	30–545		60–65
Hesperis	20–25	L	70–80
Heuchera	10 60	L	65–70
Hollyhock	10–12	L	60–70
Hypericum	30–90		50–55
Hypoestes	10–21		70–75
Impatiens	21–30	L	70–75
Incarvillea	25–30		55–65
Ipomoea	15–21		65–70
Jacaranda	10–15		70–85
Jacobaea	8–21		60–65
Kalanchoe	7–30	L	65–75
Kniphofia	10–30		65 70
Kochia	10–15	L	70–75
Larkspur	14–21	D	50–55
Lathyrus	20–30		55–65
Lavatera	15–20		65–70
Lavender	21–90		55–65
Leontopodium	10–42	L	50 55
Leptosiphon	17 21		55–65
Lettuce	4–5	L	60–65
Liatris	20–25		55–75
Lilies	30–365		65 75
Limnanthes	14–21		55–60
Linaria	10–15		55–60
Linum	20–25		55 60
Lithops	10–40	L	75–80
Lobelia	15–20	L	65–75
Lunaria	10–14		65–70
Lupin	15–60	D	55 65
Lychnis	21–30	L	65–70
Marigold	5–14		65–70
Matricaria	5–21	L	65–75
Meconopsis	14–28		55–65*
Melon	7		65–70
Mentzelia	5–21		55–60
Mesembryanthemum	15–20	D	65–75
Mimulus	7–21	L	65–70
Mirabilis	7–21	L	65–70
Moluccella	21–35	L	60–65

Variety	Germination Days	Light/ Dark	Temperature (°F)
Myosotis	14–30	D	65–70
Nasturtium	7–21	D	60–65
Nemesia	7–21	D	55–70
Nemophila	7–21		55–60
Nepeta	7–21		60–70
Nicandra	15–20		70–75
Nicotiana	10–20	L	65–70
Nigella	10–15		65–70
Nolana	14–30		60–70
Onions	2–3		55–60
Pansy	14–21	D	65–75
Papaver	10–30	D	55–60
Passiflora	30–365		70–80
Peas	4–5		60–65
Penstemon	18–21	L	55–60
Petunia	10–21	L	55–65
Phacelia	12–30	D	55–65
Phlox-Annual	10–21	D	55–65
Phlox-Perennial	25–30	D	65–70
Physalis	21–30	L	65–70
Portulaca	14–21	L	70–85
Primula	20–25	L	60–65
Pyrethum	30–60		55–60
Radish	2		55–60
Rhodanthe	14–30		75–80
Ricinus	15–21		70–75
Rudbeckia	5–21	L	65–70
Saintpaulia	30–60	L	70–75
Salpiglossis	15–30	D	70–75
Salvia	10–14	L	68–80
Saponaria	10–21	L	65–70
Saxifraga	15–60		65–75
Scabiosa	10–15		70–75
Schizanthus	7–14	D	60–75
Sedum	15–30		50–55
Silene	15–20		65–70
Solanum	15–21	L	70–75
Spinach	5–6		60–65
Stocks	10–14	L	55–60
Strelitzia	30–180		70–75
Streptocarpus	15–30	L	55–65
Sweet Pea	10–20	D	55–60

Variety	Germination Days	Light/ Dark	Temperature (°F)
Thunbergia	14–21		70–75
Thymus	15–30	L	50–55
Tomato	6–7		65–70
Tropaeolum	10–15		55–65
Turnip	2		55–60
Ursinia	14–30		55–60
Verbascum	14–30		55–60
Verbena	14–90	D	60–65
Veronica	15–30	L	65–70
Vinca	15–30	D	70–75
Viola	14–21	D	55–60
Viscaria	10–21		60–65
Zinnia	10–24		75–80

*After cold treatment

Propagation

It's not for this book to go into the details of propagation but simply to remind you which plants you can raise from seed or from one of the various forms of vegetative propagation. I have naturally left out annuals, biennials and vegetables which are nearly all raised from seed.

Bear in mind that often the seed can be collected from your own plants. Sometimes hybrids will come true to type (ie. like the parent plant the seed was collected from), as is the case with Crocosmia 'Lucifer' for example, but generally it's best to collect from species or old, established hybrids that are pollinated by insects outside. Never bother with F1 hybrids.

Cuttings are worth experimenting with. On a garden scale there's little to lose so it's worthwhile trying all methods on all plants and seeing what suits you best.

Perennials to raise from seed

Acanthus	Asphodeline	Dicentra
Achillea (but not hybrids)	Aster	Dictamnus
	Astrantia	Dierama
Aconitum	Baptisia	Digitalis
Agapanthus	Boykinia	Dodecatheon
Agastache	Calandrinia	Draba
Alchemilla	Calceolaria	Eccremocarpus
Allium	Campanula	Echinacea
Alstroemeria	Catananche	Echinops
Alyssoides	Centaurea	Epilobium
Anaphalis	Cephalaria	Eremurus
Anchusa	Cimicifuga	Erigeron
Anemone	Codonopsis	Erinus
Anthemis	Coreopsis	Erodium
Anthyllis	Corydalis	Eryngium
Aquilegia	Crocosmia	Euphorbia
Aruncus	Cynoglossum	Festuca
Asclepias	Delphinium	Filipendula

Francoa
Gaillardia
Galega
Gentiana (some)
Geranium
Geum
Helenium
Helleborus
Hesperis
Heuchera
Hieracium
Hosta
Incarvillea
Inula
Iris
Knautia
Kniphofia
Lathyrus
Leonurus
Liatris
Ligularia
Lilium
Limonium
Linaria

Linum
Liriope
Lobelia
Lupinus
Lychnis
Malva
Meconopsis
Mimulus
Miscanthus
Nepeta
Oenothera
Omphalodes
Ophiopogon
Paeonia
Papaver
Paradisea
Pennisetum
Penstemon
Phlomis
Physalis
Phytolacca
Phytostegia
Plantago
Polemonium

Potentilla
Primula
Prunella
Pulsatilla
Rodgersia
Rudbeckia
Salvia
Saponaria
Scabiosa
Semiaquilegia
Sidalcea
Silene
Sisyrinchium
Stachys
Stipa
Symphyandra
Tellima
Teucrium
Thalictrum
Tiarella
Trollius
Urospermum
Veratrum
Viola

Perennials Suitable for Basal Cuttings

Achillea
Anaphalis
Anthemis
Campanula
Chrysanthemum
Delphinium

Dicentra
Euphorbia (but
 wear gloves to
 avoid contact
 with irritant sap)
Gypsophila

Hesperis
Lupinus
Lychnis
Malva
Polygonum

Perennials Suitable for Stem Cuttings

Acaena
Achillea
Ajuga
Anthemis

Argyranthemum
Artemisia
Asarina
Aster

Astilbe
Astrantia
Ballota
Bergenia

Campanula
Carnation
Centaurea
Chrysanthemopsis
Dendranthema
Dianthus
Diascia
Draba
Eriophyllum
Euphorbia
Euryops
Felicia
Geranium

Gypsophila
Helenium
Helianthemum
Helichrysum
Iberis
Lavatera
Leucanthemum
Lobelia
Lotus
Lupinus
Lysimachia
Monarda
Osteospermum

Penstemon
Phlomis
Polygonum
Potentilla
Salvia
Saponaria
Sedum
Stachys
Tanacetum
Teucrium
Tolmiea
Veronica
Viola

Shrubs, Conifers and Climbers from Softwood Cuttings

Abies
Actindia
Akebia
Ampelopsis
Andromeda
Aristotelia
Artemisia
Berberis
Buddleia
Buxus
Callicarpa
Calluna
Calycanthus
Camellia
Campsis
Ceanothus
Celastrus
Cephalanthus
Ceratostigma
Cestrum
Chamaecyparis
Choisy
Cistus
Clematis
Convolvulus

Coprosma
Corokia
Coronilla
Cotinus
Cotoneaster
Cryptomeria
Cuphea
Cytisus
Daboecia
Deutzia
Diervilla
Dorycnium
Elaeagnus
Epilobium
Erica
Escallonia
Euonymus
Exochorda
Fatsia
Forsythia
Fuchsia
Garrya
Gaultheria
Genista
Halimiocistus

Hebe
Hedera
Helianthemum
Hibiscus
Humulus
Hydrangea
Hypericum
Ilex
Itea
Jasminum
Juniperus
Kolkwitzia
Lavandula
Lavatera
Laurus
Leycesteria
Ligustrum
Lippia
Lithospermum
Lonicera
Microbiota
Mimulus
Neillia
Olearia
Parthenocissus

Philadelphus
Phlomis
Photinia
Phygelius
Physocarpus
Picea
Pieris
Pileostegia
Pittosporum
Potentilla
Prostanthera
Pyracantha

Rhamnus
Rosa
Rosmarinus
Rubus
Ruta
Salix
Sambucus
Santolina
Sarcococca
Schizophragma
Senecio
Solanum

Spiraea
Syringa
Teucrium
Thuja
Trachelospermum
Tsuga
Ulex
Viburnum
Vinca
Vitis
Weigela
Zenobia

Shrubs from Hardwood Cuttings

Abelia
Azara
Berberis (evergreen)
Buddleia
Buxus
Cornus
Cotoneaster
Desfontainia
Deutzia
Elaeagnus
Escallonia
Forsythia

Garrya
Griselinia
Jasminum
Kerria
Leptospermum
Leycesteria
Ligustrum
Lonicera
Metasequoia
Nandina
Olearia
Osmanthus

Philadelphus
Polygonum
Ribes
Rosa
Salix
Sambucus
Sarcococca
Spiraea
Symphoricarpos
Tamarix
Viburnum (deciduous)
Weigela

Plants Suitable for Root Cuttings

Acanthus
Ailanthus
Anchusa
Anemone hybrida
Arundinaria
Brunnera
Catananche
Clerodendrum

Crambe
Dicentra
Dictamnus
Echinacea
Eryngium
Limonium
Lythrum
Nepeta

Papaver orientale
Phlox
Primula denticulata
Rhus
Robinia
Romneya
Rubus

Plants Suitable for Division

Acaena	Erigeron	Polygonatum
Achillea	Filipendula	Polygonum
Alchemilla	Geranium	Potentilla
Aquilegia	Geum	Primula
Armeria	Gladiolus	Pulmonaria
Arundinaria	Helenium	Rheum
Aster	Hemerocallis	Rodgersia
Astilbe	Hesperis	Rudbeckia
Astrantia	Heuchera	Saponaria
Bergenia	Hosta	Saxifraga
Brunnera	Koeleria	Schizostylis
Campanula	Iris	Sedum
Carex	Lamium	Sidalcea
Centaurea	Leucanthemum	Solidago
Coreopsis	Liatris	Stachys
Crocosmia	Liriope	Stipa
Dactylis	Luzula	Tanacetum
Delphinium	Lysimachia	Tellima
Dendranthema	Miscanthus	Tiarella
Dicentra	Molinia	Tradescantia
Doronicum	Oenanthe	Trollius
Echinacea	Papaver	Tropaeolum
Echinops	Phlomis	Veronica
Epimedium	Phlox	Waldsteinia

Shrubs Suitable for Semi-Ripe Cuttings

Aucuba	Convolvulus	Indigofera
Azalea (evergreen)	Cryptomeria	Itea
Berberis	Cupressocyparis	Juniperus
Buddleia	Cytisus	Kolkwitzia
Buxus	Daphne	Lavatera
Ceanothus	Escallonia	Lippia
Cedrus	Euonymus	Lonicera
Ceratostigma	Gaultheria	Myrtus
Chaenomeles	Genista	Pernettya
Chamaecyparis	Hebe	Phlomis
Choisy	Hydrangea	Philadelphus
Cistus	Hypericum	Photinia
Colutea	Ilex	Picea

Pieris	Pyracantha	Taxus
Pinus	Rhamnus	Thuja
Pittosporum	Rhododendron	Ulex
Potentilla	Ruta	Viburnum
Prunus (laurels)	Santolina	Weigela
Pseudotsuga	Senecio	

Trees and Shrubs to Raise from Seed

Acer	Daphne	Liquidamber
Aesculus	Davidia	Liriodendron
Ailanthus	Enkianthus	Morus
Alnus	Eucalyptus	Nothofagus
Amelanchier	Eucryphia	Paeonia
Arbutus	Euonymus	Paulownia
Araucaria	Fatsia	Phormium
Berberis	Fraxinus	Picea
Betula	Gaultheria	Piptanthus
Callicarpa	Genista	Pittosporum
Callistemon	Ginkgo	Prunus (some)
Carpinus	Gleditsia	Quercus
Castanea	Hibiscus	Robinia
Cercidiphyllum	Hippophae	Sorbus
Cercis	Hypericum	Spartium
Colutea	Ilex	Stranvaesia
Cornus (some)	Juglans	Taxus
Corylus	Koelreuteria	Thuja
Cotoneaster	Laburnum	Tilia
Crataegus	Larix	
Cytisus	Leycesteria	

Alpines to Raise from Seed

Acaena	Arabis	Diascia
Aethionema	Arenaria	Draba
Alyssum	Calamintha	Dryas
Anacyclus	Campanula	Erigeron
Anagallis	Chiastophyllum	Erinus
Anchusa	Cotyledon	Erysimum
Antennaria	Dianthus	Erythronium

Gentiana
Geranium
Globularia
Hepatica
Hypericum
Iberis
Leontopodium
Lewisia

Linaria
Linum
Lychnis
Papaver
Phlox
Primula
Pulsatilla
Ramonda

Saponaria
Silene
Sisyrinchium
Soldanella
Thymus
Viola

Alpines to Raise from Cuttings

Acantholimon
Achillea
Aethionema
Alyssum
Anagallis
Anchusa
Andromeda
Androsace
Arabis
Armeria
Asperula
Aubrieta
Calamintha
Campanula
Cassiope

Cotyledon
Dianthus
Draba
Dryas
Edraianthus
Erodium
Erysimum
Euryops
Frankenia
Gentiana
Geranium
Gypsophila
Helichrysum
Hypericum
Iberis

Linum
Lithospermum
Parahebe
Phlox
Polygala
Potentilla
Primula
Sagina
Saponaria
Saxifraga
Silene
Thymus
Veronica
Viola

Shrubs and Climbers to Layer

Azalea
Akebia
Camellia
Campsis
Celastrus
Clematis
Cornus
Cotinus

Hedera
Hydrangea (climbing)
Jasminum
Magnolia
Parthenocissus
Rhododendron
Ribes
Rubus

Schizophragma
Syringa
Trachelospermum
Viburnum
Vitis
Wisteria

New Roses

Every year new roses are introduced, some no better than the older ones and a few a considerable advance on them. The top priority of rose breeders these days is disease resistance so, if you wish to avoid spraying against blackspot, mildew and rust, it must be worth giving a few a trial. There may be more introductions to the rose group that are sold direct to garden centres and not listed in rose catalogues.

The addresses of the breeders are listed in the Specialist Nurseries section and you can obtain more information by sending for their catalogues. For suppliers of roses not listed here, send for the British Rose Growers Association leaflet 'Find that Rose' from The Editor, Find that Rose, 303 Mile End Rd, Colchester, Essex CO4 5EA

New Roses

BRED BY: DAVID AUSTIN ROSES

Variety	Type	Colour
Glamis Castle	Shrub	White
Golden Celebration	Shrub	Gold
Redouté	Shrub	Pale pink
Emily	Shrub	Pale pink
Sir Edward Elgar	Shrub	Crimson

INTRODUCED BY: CANTS OF COLCHESTER LTD
(Bred by Poulsen of Denmark)

Michael Crawford	Hybrid tea	Apricot/ yellow

BRED BY: JAMES COCKER & SONS

Scotland's Trust	Hybrid tea	Pale pink
Castle of Mey	Floribunda	Apricot
Shirley Spain	Floribunda	Deep pink
Toprose	Floribunda	Gold

BRED BY: DICKSON NURSERIES LTD

Variety	Type	Colour
Princess Royal	Hybrid tea	Apricot

BRED BY: FRYER'S NURSERIES LTD

Daily Post	Floribunda	Red
Julie Andrews	Floribunda	Coral
Top Marks	Miniature Patio	Orange
Fairygold	Patio	Gold

BRED BY: HARKNESS NEW ROSES LTD

Fellowship	Floribunda	Orange
High Hopes	Climber	Pink
Remembrance	Floribunda	Orange
Cordon Bleu	Hybrid tea	Apricot
High Sheriff	Hybrid tea	Coral
Cottage Garden	Patio	Copper
Sheer Delight	Patio	Orange

BRED BY: HILLS

The Newbury Angel	Patio	Yellow

INTRODUCED BY C & K JONES FROM NEW ROSE MARKETING
(Bred by Macready's)

Frothy	Miniature	White
Old Port	Floribunda	Purple
Oranges and Lemons	Floribunda	Yellow
Phantom	Ground cover shrub	Scarlet

BRED BY: MATTOCKS

Avon	Patio	White
Gwent	Ground cover	Yellow
Chiltern	Ground cover	Red
Christopher Columbus	Floribunda	Red/White
City Lights	Patio	Apricot

LAUNCHED BY: REARSBY ROSES
(Bred by Limes New Roses)

Goldfinger	Hybrid tea	Gold

BRED BY THOMAS ROBINSON

Variety	*Type*	*Colour*
Just Magic	Miniature/patio	White to Deep Pink
Royal Worcester	Shrub/patio	Pinky cream

BRED BY WARNER'S ROSES

Rosalie Coral	Climbing miniature	Gold/Copper

INTRODUCED BY: WHEATCROFT
(Bred by Tantau of Germany)

Diadem	Floribunda	Pink

Hedges

The name of the game with hedges is fast growth so make sure you prepare the soil well before planting. Dig deeply and manure a strip at least 90cm (6ft) wide.

In the following selection hedges that are generally clipped to shape are classified 'formal', while those that are allowed to grow more or less naturally are called 'informal'.

The recommended planting distances err a little on the close side for quick cover but if the budget's small, the plants could be spaced wider though they'll naturally take longer to form an impenetrable screen.

HEDGES

LOW GROWING HEDGES

Plant	Height	Planting Distance
Berberis thunbergii 'Atropurpurea Nana'	45–60cm 1–2ft	35cm 15in
Berberis verruculosa	1–1.2m 3ft	60cm 2ft
Buxus sempervirens 'Suffruticosa'	15–20cm 6–8in	15–20cm 6–8in
Hebe	60cm 2ft	45cm 1½ft
Lavandula spica	1–1.2m 3ft	45cm 1½ft
Lavandula 'Hidcote'	30–60cm 1–2ft	35cm 15in
Lavandula 'Munstead Dwarf'	45–60cm 1–2ft	35cm 15in

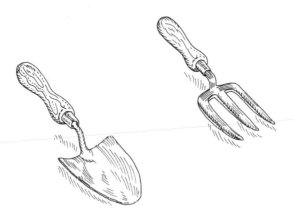

Foliage	Flowers/ Berries	Formal/ Informal	Remarks
Reddish purple	—	F	Trim in winter
Glossy green	Golden flowers in May. Attractive fruit	F	Prune in spring. Evergreen
Green	—	F	Clip in spring or late summer. Evergreen
Yellowish green	White flowers July–Sept	F	Evergreen. Trim in spring
Grey/Green	Grey/blue flowers July–Sept	F	Evergreen Trim in spring
Silvery	Deep purple/blue flowers	F	Evergreen. Trim in spring
Grey/green	Dark flowers	F	Evergreen. Trim in spring

Plant	Height	Planting Distance
Lavandula vera	60–90cm 2–3ft	35cm 15in
Potentilla 'Farreri'	1–1.2m 3–3½ft	60cm 2ft
Potentilla 'Jackman's Star'	1–1.2m 3–3½ft	60cm 2ft
Prunus cistena	1.2–1.5m 3½–4½ft	60cm 2ft
Santolina chamaecyparissus	45–60cm 1½–2ft	30cm 1ft
Santolina chamaecyparissus 'Nana'	30–45cm 1–1½ft	23cm 9in
Santolina virens	45cm 1½ft	30cm 1ft

TALL HEDGES (INFORMAL)

Plant	Height	Planting Distance
Berberis darwinii	1.2–1.8m 4–6ft	60cm 2ft
Berberis sanguinea	1.2m 4ft	60cm 2ft
Berberis stenophylla	3m 10ft	60cm 2ft
Berberis thunbergii	1.2–1.8m 4–6ft	60cm 2ft
Berberis thunbergii 'Atropurpurea'	1.5–2m 5–6ft	60cm 2ft
Berberis thunbergii 'Erecta'	60cm–1.2m 2–4ft	45cm 1½ft

Foliage	Flowers/ Berries	Formal/ Informal	Remarks
Silvery	Soft blue flowers	F	Trim in April. Deadhead all season
Fern-like	Yellow flowers May–Sept	F	Prune in spring
Fern-like	Brilliant yellow flowers	F or I	Prune in spring
Crimson	White flowers	F or I	Trim after flowering
Feathery Silver	Yellow flowers June–Aug	F or I	Trim after flowering and in April Evergreen
Feathery Silver	Yellow flowers June–Aug	F or I	Trim after flowering and in April. Evergreen
Bright green	Lemon yellow flowers	F or I	Trim after flowering and in April

Foliage	Flowers/ Berries	Formal/ Informal	Remarks
Shield-like Shiny green	Orange/yellow flowers April/May Bluish/purple berries	I	Prune after flowering Trim in winter Evergreen Impenetrable
Sea green	Greenish	I	Evergreen
Deep green	Yellow flowers May/June	I	Prune after flowering Evergreen Impenetrable
	Pale yellow flowers. Bright red fruit	I	Impenetrable
Reddish purple		I	
		I	Stiff vertical habit makes a narrow hedge

Plant	Height	Planting Distance
Berberis thunbergii 'Helmond Pillar'	60cm–1.2m 2–4ft	45cm 1½ft
Berberis thunbergii 'Red Chief'	1.5–2m 5–6ft	60cm 2ft
Cotoneaster lacteus	2.5–3m 8–10ft	90cm 3ft
Cotoneaster simonsii	1.5–2.5m 5–6ft	45cm 1½ft
Escallonia varieties	1.5–1.8m 5–6ft	75cm 2½ft
Euonymus japonicus 'Ovatus Aureus'	1.5–2.5m 5–8ft	45cm 1½ft
Griselinia littoralis	3.5–4.5m 11–14ft	60cm 2ft
Hebe speciosa	1.2m 4ft	60cm 2ft
Hippophae rhamnoides	1.8–2.2m 6–7ft	60cm 2½ft
Ilex aquifolium	1.5m 5ft	90cm 3ft
Olearia haastii	1.2m 3½ft	90cm 3ft
Osmanthus burkwoodii	1.8–2.4m 6–8ft	60cm 2ft
Pittosporum tenuifolium	1.5–2.5m 5–8ft	45cm 1½ft
Prunus cerasifera 'Pissardii'	1.8–2.5m 6–8ft	60cm 2ft

Foliage	Flowers/ Berries	Formal/ Informal	Remarks
Reddish bronze form of 'Erecta'		I	
Wine red form of 'Atropurpurea'		I	
Olive green	White flowers in June Red berries		Prune in summer Impenetrable. Evergreen
Turns red in winter	Red berries	I	Trim in winter. Evergreen
Green	Pink or white flowers	F or I	Prune after flowering and lightly in spring. Evergreen
Green		I	Good for seaside. Trim in spring. Evergreen
Fresh green		I	Use only near sea. Trim early summer
Green above, purple beneath	Pink, red or purple flowers	I	Suitable only for mild areas. Evergreen
Silvery white	Orange flowers Red berries	I	Good for seaside. Trim in spring
Dark green	Red berries	F or I	Trim late summer Impenetrable Evergreen
Greyish Oval	White flowers July onwards	I	Prune after flowering Evergreen
Lustrous green Toothed	Scented white flowers April/May	I	Trim after flowering Evergreen
Pale shiny green	Purple flowers in May Black berries	I	Prune as required Needs light soil and shelter. Evergreen Only for mild areas
Purple	Pink flowers in spring	F or I	Trim after flowering

Plant	Height	Planting Distance
Prunus lusitanica	1.5–1.8m 5–8ft	60cm 2ft
Prunus laurocerasus 'Rotundifolia'	1.5–1.8m 5–8ft	60cm 2ft
Pyracantha rogersiana	1.2–1.8m 4–6ft	60cm 2ft
Rhododendron luteum	2.2–2.4m 7–8ft	90cm 3ft
Rhododendron ponticum	1.8–3m 6–9ft	90cm 3ft
Rosmarinus officinalis 'Miss Jessop's Upright'	1.2–1.8m 4–6ft	60cm 2ft
Symphoricarpos 'Magic Berry'	1.2–1.5m 4–5ft	1m 3ft
Symphoricarpos 'White Hedge'	1.2–1.5m 4–5ft	1m 3ft
Syringa vulgaris varieties	2.5–3m 8–10ft	1.2m 4ft
Tamarix gallica	1.2–1.5m 3?–4ft	60cm 2ft
Tamarix pentandra	1.2–1.5m 3?–4ft	60cm 2ft
Viburnum tinus	1.8–2.5m 6–8ft	60cm 2ft
Viburnum tinus 'Eve Price'	1.8–2.5m 6–8ft	60cm 2ft

Foliage	Flowers/ Berries	Formal/ Informal	Remarks
Dark glossy green	Scented white flowers in June Purple berries	I	Prune in April Evergreen
Light green Broad		I	Prune in April. Evergreen
Glossy green	White flowers in June. Red berries		Prune in spring and summer if necessary. Evergreen
Good autumn colour	Scented yellow flowers May/June	I	Needs lime-free soil. Deciduous
Dark glossy green	Purplish pink flowers	I	Evergreen. Needs lime-free soil
Dark green White underside	Blue flowers in May	F	Trim in spring Evergreen
Green	Lilac flowers Carmine berries	I	Trim in Spring
Green	White berries	I	Trim in spring
Green	White, pink or mauve flowers. May–June	I	Prune after flowering
Feathery Sea green	Pink flowers June–Aug	I	Good for seaside. Prune hard in spring
Silvery grey	Rose pink flowers		
Oval Dark glossy green	Pink buds White flowers. Blue berries Dec–March	I	Evergreen
	Carmine buds Pink flowers		

TALL HEDGES (FORMAL)

Plant	Height	Planting Distance
Acer campestre	1.8–3m 6–10ft	60cm 2ft
Carpinus betulus	1.5–2.5m 5–8ft	45cm 1½ft
Crataegus monogyna	1.5–2.5m 5–8ft	30cm 12in
Fagus sylvatica	2–3m 7–10ft	45cm 1½ft
Fagus sylvatica 'Riversii'	2–3m 7–10ft	45cm 1½ft
Ligustrum ovalifolium	1.2–1.8m 4–6ft	30cm 1ft
Ligustrum ovalifolium 'Aureum'	1.2–1.8m 4–6ft	30cm 1ft
Lonicera nitida	1.2–1.8m 4–6ft	30cm 1ft

CONIFEROUS

Plant	Height	Planting Distance
Chamaecyparis lawsoniana 'Alumii'	2.5m 8ft	90cm 3ft
Chamaecyparis lawsoniana 'Fletcheri'	2.5m 8ft	90cm 3ft
Chamaecyparis lawsoniana 'Green Hedger'	2.5m 8ft	90cm 3ft
Cupressocyparis × leylandii	3.5–4.5m 12–15ft	90cm 3ft

Foliage	Flowers/ Berries	Formal/ Informal	Remarks
Red in spring Orange–red in autumn		F	Trim in winter or summer
Green		F	Trim in winter or late summer. Good alternative to beech on wet soil
Green	Scented white flowers	F	A field hedge
Brown leaves last all winter		F	Avoid heavy wet soils
Light red turning to purple		F	Avoid heavy wet soils
Green		F	Semi-Evergreen. Trim in April and August
Yellow		F	Semi-Evergreen. Trim in April and August
Glossy Small Green		F	Trim April and August Evergreen

Foliage	Flowers/ Berries	Formal/ Informal	Remarks
Blue–grey and sea green		F	Evergreen
Grey–green Feathery		F	Evergreen
Bright green		F	Evergreen
Grey–green		F	Fast growing. Good for coastal areas. Evergreen

Plant	Height	Planting Distance
Cupressocyparis × leylandii 'Castlewellan'	3.5–4.5m 12–15ft	90cm 3ft
Cupressus macrocarpa 'Gold Crest'	3m 10ft	90cm 3ft
Pinus nigra 'Austriaca'	2.5–3m 8–10ft	1.5m 5ft
Pinus radiata	3.5–4.5m 12–15ft	1.5m 5ft
Taxus baccata (Yew)	1.8m 6ft	60cm 2ft
Thuja occidentalis 'Smaragd'	2.5–3m 8–10ft	90cm 3ft
Thuja plicata 'Atrovirens'	2.5–3m 8–10ft	90cm 3ft

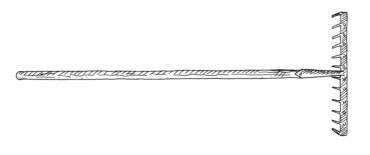

Foliage	Flowers/ Berries	Formal/ Informal	Remarks
Golden			
Bright golden		F	Trim with secateurs at first in April and August. Evergreen
Dark green		I	Shape in spring. Good for coast. More used for a windbreak
Grassy green		I	Evergreen. A good windbreak for seaside areas
Dark green		F	Trim late summer. Needs good drainage. Evergreen
Emerald green		F	Evergreen
Bright dark green		F	Fast growing. Trim with secateurs in summer

Greenhouse Temperatures

What you grow in your greenhouse depends entirely on the temperatures you can maintain during the winter. Bear in mind that it's the minimum temperature that's important and it generally only needs to dip below that recommended at night for the damage to be done. Plants are killed and will not recover.

The easiest and cheapest way is to grow only hardy plants in winter and to move them out in the spring when they can be replaced with more tender plants. This still leaves plenty of scope for, say, alpines in winter and tomatoes and pot plants in summer.

If you decide to add heat in order to keep more tender plants through the winter, you'll naturally extend your scope tremendously. But make sure that you have a back-up in case of really cold nights.

Choose a heater of a size that should produce the correct temperature and supplement that with a small, thermostatically-controlled, extra one. Set it so that it only comes on when the temperature falls below the necessary level and you sleep easy at nights.

The temperatures quoted here are all minimums.

Plants for particular Temperature Regimes

Temperatures will need to be higher for propagation

BELOW 32°F (0°C)	Correa	Ferns
Hardy bulbs	Daphne	Habrothamnus
Most alpines	Desfontainea	Lapageria
Hardy perennials and shrubs	Dionaea	Leonotis
	Diosma	Leucophyta
40°F (7°C)	Erica	Mimulus
Abelia	Eriostemon	Nertera
Acacia	Eugenia	Olea
Bambusa	Eulalia	Ophiopogon
Callistemon	Fabiana	Ornithogalum
Coronilla	Fatsia	Oxalis

Pelargonium
Polygala
Punica
Rehmannia
Richardia
Selaginella
Sollya
Sparmannia
Statice
Streptocarpus
Trachelium
Vallota

45°F (7°C)
Agapetes
Agathaea
Aloe
Aloysia
Anigozanthus
Anthericum
Araucaria
Ardisia
Asclepias
Azalea
Billbergia
Boronia
Bougainvillea
Bouvardia
Brunfelsia
Burchellia
Calceolaria
Calendula
Campanula
Campsis
Carex
Carnation
Cassia
Celsia
Centradenia
Ceropegia
Chamaedorea
Chlorophytum
Choisya
Chorizema

Cineraria
Cissus
Clarkia
Clematis
Clivia
Cobaea
Colocasia
Cotyledon
Crassula
Crinum
Cuphea
Cymbidium
Cytisus
Darlingtonia
Datura
Drosera
Echeveria
Epacris
Epidendrum
Epiphyllum
Erythrina
Eucalyptus
Eurya
Ferns
Francoa
Freesia
Fuchsia
Gerbera
Gesnera
Gilia
Grevillea
Haemanthus
Hedychium
Hibbertia
Hoya
Humea
Isolepis
Jasminum
Justicia
Kleinia
Lachenalia
Lagerstroemia
Lantana
Lilium

Luculia
Lycoris
Mandevilla
Manettia
Milla
Mitraria
Myrtus
Nerine
Nerium
Odontoglossum
Opuntia
Pachyphytum
Parodia
Passiflora
Pavetta
Pelargonium
Petrea
Pharbitis
Pilea
Pimelea
Plumbago
Polianthes
Portulacaria
Pycnostachys
Reineckea
Reseda
Rhodochiton
Rhododendron
Russelia
Salvia
Sarracenia
Saxifraga
Scutellaria
Selaginella
Selenicereus
Sparmannia
Stenocarpus
Stephanotis
Streptosolen
Thyrsacanthus
Tibouchina
Trachelium
Trachelospermum
Tristania

Veronica
Zebrina
Zephyranthes

50°F (10°C)
Achimenes
Adiantum
Aechmea
Agave
Aphelandra
Aporocactus
Asparagus
Aspidistra
Begonia
Beloperone
Browallia
Brunfelsia
Camellia
Celosia
Citrus
Clianthus
Coleus
Cryptanthus
Cyclamen
Cyperus
Eustoma
Exacum
Ficus
Gloriosa
Gloxinia
Hatiora
Heliotropium
Hippeastrum
Hylocereus
Hymenocallis
Impatiens
Jacaranda

Jacobinia
Kalanchoe
Lotus
Monstera
Neoregelia
Nidularium
Ochna
Palms
Persea
Platycerium
Primula
Rhipsalis
Schlumbergera
Sinningia
Solanum
Strelitzia
Streptocarpus
Tradescantia
Zantedeschia

55°F (13°C)
Alpinia
Amasonia
Begonia
  (fibrous-rooted)
Caladium
Clerodendrum
Codiaeum
Crossandra
Desmodium
Dicentra
Dieffenbachia
Dipladenia
Eranthemum
Eucharis
Euphorbia

Ferns
  (stove species)
Ficus
Fittonia
Gardenia
Gynura
Heliconia
Hibiscus
Hoya
  (stove species)
Hydrangea
Ipomoea
Ixora
Jasminum
  (stove species)
Lachenalia
Leea
Maranta
Mussaenda
Pandanus
Panicum
Passiflora
  (stove species)
Pellionia
Peperomia
Plumbago
  (stove species)
Rondeletia
Ruellia
Sanchezia
Sansevieria
Sonerila
Stigmaphyllon
Strelitzia
Thunbergia
Zingiber

60°F (16°C)
Acalypha
Aechmea
Aeschynanthus
Aglaonema
Allamanda
Alocasia
Alonsoa
Ananas
Anthurium
Aphelandra
Aralia
Aristolochia
Azalea
Bauhinia
Bertolonia
Canna
Columnea
Cryptanthus
Medinilla
Musa
Nidularium
Philodendron
Phyllanthus
Saintpaulia
Schismatoglottis
Strobilanthes
Tabernaemontana
Tillandsia
Trevesia
Vriesia

65°F (18°C)
Dracaena
Ipomoea (some)
Nepenthes

Greenhouses and Greenhouse Equipment

The products listed here have all been tried and tested at Barnsdale and are considered good value for money. However, exclusion from the list does not necessarily imply that a product is inferior.

(GC = obtainable at garden centres)

Greenhouses

Banbury Homes & Gardens Ltd,
PO Box 17, Banbury, Oxfordshire
OX17 3NS
Robinsons of Winchester, Chilcomb
Lane, Chilcomb, Winchester,
Hampshire SO21 1HU (Aluminium).
Cambridge Glasshouse Co, Barton Rd,
Comberton, Cambridgeshire CB3 7BY

Polythene tunnels
LBS Polythene, Cottontree, Colne,
Lancashire BB8 7BW

Greenhouse equipment

Automatic ventilators
Bayliss Precision Components,
Lysander Works, Blenheim Rd,
Airfield Industrial Estate, Ashbourne,
Derbyshire DE6 1HA
Jemp Engineering, Canal Estate,
Station Rd, Langley, Berkshire
SL3 6EG

Thermoforce, Heybridge Works,
Maldon, Essex CM9 7NW

Disinfectant
Jeyes Fluid. GC.

Fertilisers
Fisons Liquinure. GC.
Fisons Tomorite. GC.
Phostrogen. GC.

Heaters
Jemp Engineering Ltd, Canal Estate,
Station Rd, Langley, Berkshire
SL3 6FG (electric).
George H. Elt Ltd, Eltex Works,
Bromyard Rd, Worcester WR2 5DN
(paraffin and gas).

Hormone rooting liquid
PBI Roota. GC.

Instruments (thermometers etc)
Diplex, PO Box 172, Watford,
Hertfordshire WD1 1BX

Insulation
Nortene. GC.

Lighting
Sunlight Systems, 3, St. Mary's Works, Burnmoor St, Leicester LE2 7JJ

Modules
PG Horticulture, Street Farm, Thornham Magna, Eye, Suffolk IP23 8HB. (plastic)
AP Propapacks, (polystyrene). GC.

Propagators
George Ward (Moxley) Ltd, Heathfield Lane, Darlaston, West Midlands WS10 8QZ GC.

Propagating blanket to make heated bench
Prylorn Ltd, Elmhurst Yard, High St, Chatteris, Cambridgeshire PE16 6NP

Seed trays
George Ward (Moxley) Ltd, Heathfield Lane, Darlaston, West Midlands WS10 8QZ. GC.

Shading
PBI Coolglass. GC.

Soil warming cable
Jemp Engineering Ltd, Canal Estate, Station Rd, Langley, Berkshire SL3 6EG

Sprayers
Hozelock-ASL. GC.

Staging and accessories
Two Wests and Elliott, Unit 4, Carrwood Rd, Sheepbridge Industrial Estate, Chesterfield, Derbyshire S41 9RH

Terracotta Pots
Whichford Pottery, Whichford, Shipston-on-Stour, Warwickshire CV36 5PG Olive Tree. GC.

Watering cans
Haws, 120, Beakes Rd, Smethwick, Warley, West Midlands B67 5AB Geeco. GC.

Watering systems (automatic)
Hozelock-ASL. GC.

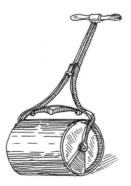

Concrete

The following mixes have been used at Barnsdale and other gardens over the years and have proved successful over a long term. All the measurements are by volume and note that it's absolutely essential to use *fresh* cement.

For the base to paving:
8 parts all-in ballast.
1 part Portland cement.
Mix dry and spread at least 7.5cm (3in) thickness. Consolidate by treading.

Mortar for laying paving:
3 parts builders sand.
1 part Portland cement.
Mix quite dry.

For setting fence posts:
6 parts all-in ballast.
1 part Portland cement.
Mix on the dry side consistent with ease of tamping down. Ideally concrete in metal sockets to take the wooden posts.

For foundations of walling and areas of exposed concrete:
6 parts all-in ballast.
1 part Portland cement.
Mix as dry as possible consistent with ease of laying. In freezing weather use liquid antifreeze in gauging water as instructions on can. If required, colouring powder can also be added.

Mortar for laying brick and stone walling:
3 parts builders sand.
1 part masonry cement.
For bricks, mix the mortar quite wet but make it much drier for stone.

For building concrete pools:
6 parts all-in ballast.
1 part Portland cement.
Concrete waterproofer used as instructions on the can.
Use this for the main structure of the pool and then skim over the top with a screed of:
3 parts sharp sand.
1 part Portland cement.
Liquid waterproofer added to gauging water as instructions on can.

For making 'hypa-tufa' troughs or covering glazed sinks:
2 parts sieved coir compost.
2 parts sharp sand.
1 part Portland cement.

ADDITIVES:
A variety of concrete additives is available for colouring, to protect against frost, to speed drying, to increase hardening and to plasticise mortar for easy and clean brickwork. Ask at any builders merchant.

Landscape Gardening Equipment

The manufacturers and suppliers mentioned here are those who have provided materials for work carried out at Barnsdale or one of our other projects shown on *Gardeners' World*.

Arbours and garden buildings
The English Basket Centre, The Willows, Curload, Stoke St Gregory, Taunton, Somerset TA3 6JD.
Chatsworth Carpenters, Estate Office, Edensor, Bakewell, Derbyshire DE1 1PH.
Stuart Garden Architecture, Larchfield Estate, Dowlish Ford, Ilminster, Somerset TA19 0PF.

Concrete Pavers
Marshalls Mono, Southowram, Halifax, West Yorkshire HX3 9SY.

Fencing
Forest Fencing Ltd, Stanford Court, Stanford Bridge, Nr Worcester WR6 6SR.
Larch-Lap Ltd, PO Box 17, Lichfield St, Stourport-on-Severn, Hereford & Worcester DY13 9ES.
The English Basket Centre, The Willows, Curload, Stoke St Gregory, Nr. Taunton, Somerset TA3 6JD. (Willow hurdles).

Fruit cages and arches
Agriframes, Charlwoods Rd, East Grinstead, West Sussex RH19 2HG.

Furniture
Andrew Crace Designs, 49 Bourne Lane, Much Hadham, Hertfordshire SG10 6ER.
Barlow Tyrie Ltd, Springwood Industrial Estate, Rayne Rd, Braintree, Essex CM7 7RN.
Lister, Green Bros Ltd, South Rd, Hailsham, East Sussex BN27 4DT.
Seat-table, Unit D3, Plumtree Farm Industrial Estate, Bircotes, Doncaster, South Yorkshire DN11 8EW.

Grass seed
Planting Ideas Ltd, Stepfields, Witham, Essex CM8 3TA.
W W Johnson and Son, London Rd, Boston, Lincolnshire PE21 8AD.

Gravel, decorative
Border Hardcore and Rockery Stone Co, Middletown Quarry, Welshpool, Powys SY21 8DJ.

Manhole covers
Drainplanters, Quigley Plastics,
Newtown Industrial Estate, Cross
Keys, Newport, Gwent NP1 7PZ.

Ornaments
Chilstone Garden Ornaments, Spivers
Estate, Lamberhurst Rd, Hormonsden,
Kent TN12 8DR.
Haddonstone Ltd, The Forge House,
East Haddon, Northamptonshire
NN6 8DB.
Minsterstone Ltd, Station Rd,
Ilminster, Somerset TA19 9AS.

Paving and walling
Bradstone Garden Products, Okus
Trading Estate, Swindon, Wiltshire
SN1 4JH.
Marley, Stifford Rd, South Ockendon,
Essex RM15 6RL.
Marshalls Mono, Southowram,
Halifax, West Yorkshire HX3 9SY.
The Marley Paving Co. Ltd, Lichfield
Rd, Branston, Burton-on-Trent,
Staffordshire DE14 3HD.

Pergolas
Forset Fencing. GC.
Larchlap. GC.

Pools and pool liners
Stapeley Water Gardens Ltd,
92 London Rd, Stapeley, Nantwich,
Cheshire CW5 6HE.
Lotus Water Garden Products,
PO Box 36, Junction St, Burnley,
Lancashire BB12 0NA.

Printed Concrete
Creteprint, Auckland House, Perry
Way, Witham, Essex CM8 3SX.

Stone, Natural
Border Stone, Middletown Quarry,
Welshpool, Powys SY21 8DJ.
J. Brailsford Turf Ltd, Thrang End
Farm, Yealand Redmayne, Carnforth,
Lancashire LA5 9TE.
Stonecraft, Burgh Rd, Aylesham,
Norfolk NR11 6AR.

Trellis
Stuart Garden Architecture, Larchfield
Estate, Dowlish Ford, Ilminster,
Somerset TA19 0PF.
Frolics of Winchester, 82 Canon St,
Winchester, Hampshire SO23 9JQ.
Hickson Landscape Structures,
Wheldon Rd, Castleford, West
Yorkshire WF10 2JT.
See also 'Fencing'.

Tubs and troughs (plastic)
Grosfillex UK Ltd, 10 Chandos Rd,
London NW10 6NF.
(glazed ceramic): Woodlodge Products,
21B Rydens Rd, Walton-on-Thames,
Surrey KT12 3AB.
(terracotta): Whichford Pottery,
Whichford, Shipston-on-Stour,
Warwickshire CV36 5PG.

Turf
Rolawn (Turf Growers) Ltd,
Elvington, Yorkshire YO4 5AR.

Seasonal Gardening Jobs

It's difficult to advise accurately times to carry out gardening jobs, simply because the weather and climate vary so much. Cold, exposed areas could be as much as two, three or even four weeks behind warmer places. So the jobs are listed in seasons rather than months. You'll soon get used to your own timings and can use this list as a reminder. As a guide, the following months apply to Barnsdale which is in a relatively exposed spot in the east midlands.

Winter – November to late January.
Early spring – February to late March.
Spring – April to late May.

Early summer – June to early July.
Summer – July to late August.
Autumn – September to late October.

WINTER

Kitchen garden
Protect all members of the cabbage family with netting against hungry birds.
● Order seed catalogues.
● Clear away debris and make regular slug and snail-hunting sorties.
● Plant fruit trees and bushes.
● Lift a few parsnips and leeks and put them into a corner in garden compost in case the ground freezes hard.
● Winter prune bush apples and pears.
● Remove the top netting of the fruit cage in case it snows.
● Keep strawberries in pots outside but put them on their sides to prevent waterlogging.
● Protect cauliflower curds from frost by snapping a few leaves over them.
● Continue winter digging and manuring.
● Remove all weeds to the compost heap.
● Remove stumps of brassicas immediately after harvesting and shred them if possible.
● Plant new rhubarb crowns.
● Cover a piece of ground with clear polythene for the early crops.

Flower garden
● Sweep up fallen leaves and put them into a container.
● Cover alpines that resent winter wet.
● Clear all debris from the borders and lightly fork over spreading manure or compost at the same time.
● Winter prune deciduous shrubs.

● Plant trees and shrubs.

● Be prepared to protect plants in the cold-frame against frost by covering.

● Sow seeds of berried shrubs and alpines and put the pots outside or in the frame.

● Check stakes and ties on trees and replace or loosen as necessary.

● Brush snow off trees and shrubs if it threatens to damage them. Otherwise leave them covered as insulation.

● Remove all weeds to the compost heap.

● Shrubs that are in the wrong place can now be moved.

● Protect tender plants with cloches.

● Take hardwood cuttings.

Greenhouse, windowsill and potting shed

● Ventilate as much as possible during the day but leave only the smallest chink at night. Some heating may be necessary to maintain frost-free conditions.

● Insulate with bubble polythene to save heating costs.

● If you have border space sow broad beans, early peas and winter lettuce.

● Examine stored fruit and vegetables and remove any showing signs of rotting.

● If your seed order arrives, store it in a cold, dry place.

● Check dahlia tubers in store.

● Sow cyclamen if you can maintain a temperature of 18C(64F).

● Clean pots and boxes in very hot water with a little household bleach added.

● Take advantage of sunny days to do any greenhouse repairs.

● Plant figs, vines, peaches and nectarines and pot up citrus fruits.

● Put greasebands on the staging legs to protect against vine weevils.

● Set up potato tubers to sprout.

● Towards the end of the period, sow hardy annuals in modules.

● Sow broad beans, cabbage, carrot cauliflower, celery, celeriac, lettuce, spinach, onion, pea, salad onion and turnip.

● Take root cuttings of perennials.

General

● Check tools, repair them if necessary and put them away.

● Take the mower to be serviced.

● Buy in manure and stack it.

● Check the garden centre for winter bargains and try to buy the next season's requirements all at once while they're a bit cheaper.

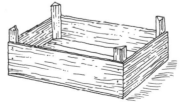

EARLY SPRING

Kitchen garden

- Try to finish off the winter digging as soon as possible.
- Put out cloches for early vegetables at least 2 weeks in advance of sowing or planting.
- Plant potatoes.
- Test for lime and spread it if necessary.
- Feed fruit trees and bushes.
- Plant Jerusalen artichokes.
- Cover strawberries with cloches.
- When the soil has warmed up sufficiently under cloches, sow broad bean, carrot, cabbage, cauliflower, lettuce, early peas, salad onions, spinach and turnips. If you sowed the same crops in the greenhouse, plant them out at the same time.
- Plant onion sets and shallots outside if the weather and soil conditions are favourable.
- Protect peaches from rain to avoid peach leaf curl fungus.
- Prune autumn fruiting raspberries.
- Net blackcurrants against bullfinches which eat the buds.
- Feed spring cabbage with a high nitrogen fertilizer.
- Sow parsnips and hamburg parsley.
- Plant perennial herbs.
- Towards the end of the period, sow winter cabbage, cauliflower, kale, brussels sprouts, sprouting broccoli and leeks in a seed-bed.
- Plant out globe artichokes and onion sets towards the end of the period.
- Lift, divide and replant chives, garlic chives and sorrel.
- Graft apples and pears.

Flower garden

- Prune deciduous shrubs that flower later in the year on the current season's growth.
- Prune hypericums back to the ground if they were infected with rust disease.
- Prune late-flowering clematis.
- Lift and transplant snowdrops, snowflakes and aconites.
- Sow sweet peas or transplant those raised inside from an earlier sowing.
- Towards the end of the period, sow hardy annuals or plant out seedlings raised earlier inside.
- Prune roses. Plant new herbaceous perennials and lift and divide congested clumps.
- Replace rockery plants.
- Hard prune shrubs grown for their winter bark colour.
- Rake the lawn to remove old thatch. You may also be able to mow.
- Lay turf lawns unless the soil is frozen.
- Trim winter flowering heathers as soon as they finish flowering.
- Towards the end of the period, plant gladioli.
- Plant lilies outside if the weather's favourable. If not, pot them up for planting later.
- Feed all plants in the borders not forgetting the hedges.

Greenhouse, windowsill and potting shed

- Ventilate freely on sunny days but still close up almost completely at night. Check frames and cloches on sunny days and ventilate if necessary.

● Sow begonias and geraniums in a heated propagator.
● Pick over rooted cuttings, removing diseased leaves.
● Take cuttings of chrysanthemums, dahlias, fuchsias, geraniums and most tender perennials.
● Towards the end of the period sow cucumbers, melons and tomatoes for growing in the cool greenhouse.
● Sow half-hardy annuals.
● Repot fruit plants if necessary.
● Take basal cuttings of perennials.
● Sow seeds of perennials for flowering later this year.
● Sow tender perennials like salvia, eccremocarpus and rhodochiton for flowering later this year.
● Take cuttings of heathers.

General
● Put down tiles or slates to catch slugs and turn them over each morning.

SPRING

Kitchen garden
● Sow maincrop varieties of beetroot, broad bean, carrot, chicory, florence fennel, french beans, kohl rabi, lettuce, onion, pea, radish, salad onion, salsify, scorzonera, spinach, summer cabbage, summer cauliflower, swiss chard and turnip.
● Thin out or transplant seedlings as necessary.
● Continue to plant early potatoes.
● Prune cherries and plums.
● Plant onions raised in the greenhouse or frame.
● Mulch with compost or manure around rhubarb.
● Apply water in dry weather.

● Sow dill, hyssop, parsley, rue, marjoram and thyme.
● Plant asparagus.
● During the day remove cloches from strawberries to allow the entry of pollinating insects. Tuck straw underneath ripening fruit.
● Towards the end of the period sow swedes.
● When weather conditions permit, plant courgettes, tomatoes, cucumbers, french beans, runner beans and squashes under cloches and sow the same vegetables outside.
● Pinch out tops of broad beans attacked by blackfly.
● Protect carrots, parsnips, celeriac, hamburg parsley and parsley against carrot fly attack.
● Put out codling moth traps.
● Earth up potatoes and protect them against frost if necessary.
● Plant leeks and brassicas from the seed bed.
● Plant self-blanching celery and protect against carrot fly.
● Take cuttings of mint and rosemary.

● Take measures to control apple and pear scab.

● Tie in new growth of briar fruits as they develop.

Flower garden

● Thin out hardy annual seedlings sown earlier.

● Remove flowers of bulbs as they fade to prevent seeding unless self-set seedlings are required.

● Plant acidanthera, crocosmia, galtonia, gladioli, nerine and ornithogalum.

● Plant evergreens and shift large plants if necessary.

● Plant sweet peas.

● Plant our crysanthemums, argyranthemums and euryops.

● Mow the lawn regularly and feed and weed.

● Take conifer cuttings.

● Finish lifting, dividing and transplanting hardy perennials.

● Continue turfing and sow new lawns.

● Prune spring-flowering deciduous shrubs as soon as they finish flowering.

● Stake hardy herbaceous perennials as they grow.

● Plant aquatic and bog plants and remove blanket weed from the pond.

● Towards the end of the period sow hardy perennials and biennials in a seed bed outside.

● Prune early flowering clematis after it's finished flowering.

● Lift, divide and replant polyanthus.

● Lift bulbs that have finished flowering where space is needed and heel them into a corner of the vegetable plot.

● Plant out hardy perennials raised from seed in the greenhouse.

● Trim alpines if they're spreading beyond their allotted space.

● Tie in climbers regularly.

Greenhouse, windowsill and potting shed

● Ventilate the greenhouse as much as possible and keep floors and staging moist to create humidity.

● Sow sweet corn and tomatoes for planting outside.

● Continue to prick out and repot plants as necessary.

● Continue sowing half hardy annuals for outside planting and for pot plants.

● Take dahlia cuttings.

● Take conifer cuttings.

● Plant tomatoes and cucumbers in the border or in growing bags and pot up peppers and aubergines all in the cold greenhouse.

● Control whitefly.

● From the middle to the end of the period, shift half-hardy plants to the cold frame to harden off before planting out.

● Cover frame if frost is threatened.

● If you have room towards the end of the period, plant up hanging baskets and tubs and keep them inside until all danger of frost is gone.

● Remove sideshoots from tomatoes and start feeding them together with the cucumbers, peppers and aubergines.

● Sow calceolarias, cinerarias and primulas for pot plants.

● Start to prune grapes.

● If plants waiting to be planted begin to look yellow, give them a liquid feed.

General

● Keep topping up the compost heaps. If both become full, empty out the one that's most rotted and stack it outside until use.

● Keep on top of the weeds by regular hoeing or hand pulling.

● Check all new plantings and water regularly.

EARLY SUMMER

Kitchen garden

● Plant out runner beans, tomatoes, cucumbers, courgettes, marrows and sweet corn.

● Continue sowing radish and spinach but now in a shady spot.

● Peg down runners of strawberries to make new plants for forcing.

● Control greenfly and other pests.

● Continue sowing beetroot, carrot, chicory, endive, lettuce, swedes and turnips.

● Sow chicory for forcing and spinach beet for autumn use.

● Sow chinese cabbage, french beans, swiss chard, rhubarb chard and some spring cabbage in a seed bed.

● Net fruit bushes against birds.

● Pick the first gooseberries for ripening and leave some to eat fresh later.

● Protect newly planted brassicas from cabbage root fly.

● Harvest and store shallots and harvest early potatoes.

● Remove flower spikes from rhubarb.

● As tomatoes grow, take out the sideshoots from the upright growers and tuck straw underneath the bush varieties.

● Pick and dry herbs as they become ready.

● Sow carrots, turnips and beetroot for winter storage.

● Harvest globe artichokes before the flowers start to open.

● At the end of the period start to sow some early varieties of vegetables for lifting in autumn.

● Sow a few broad beans for the harvest of green tops they provide in autumn.

● After strawberries have finished cropping, cut off the old leaves and clean the beds.

● Pinch out the tips of runner beans when they reach the top of the canes.

● Harvest and prune raspberries as they ripen.

● Summer prune pears.

Flower garden

● Plant out half hardy annuals and tender perennials.

● Put out planted tubs and hanging baskets and start watering daily and feeding weekly.

● Take softwood cuttings of shrubs.

● Prune brooms that have finished flowering.

● Continue to trim and tie herbaceous

plants cutting them down after flowering unless you intend to save seed.

● Divide and replant *Iris germanica* rhizomes.

● Plant corms of *Anemone coronaria*.

● Take stem cuttings of pinks. Tie in climbers regularly.

● Top up the pool and bog garden in dry weather.

● Propagate climbers by layering.

● Plant perennials and biennials sown earlier into a nursery bed.

● Stake gladioli and other tall summer bulbs.

● Disbud chrysanthemums and dahlias for larger blooms.

● Mound up alpines that are going bare in the middle, dropping a little compost into the bare areas.

● Prune summer-flowering deciduous shrubs.

● Dead head roses and annual bedding to extend flowering.

● Take cuttings of hydrangeas.

● Layer border carnations.

● Collect and sow seed of some perennials.

● Take half-ripe cuttings of shrubs.

● Cut back straggly growth of arabis, aubrieta and violas.

● Plant autumn-flowering bulbs.

Greenhouse, windowsill and potting shed

● Ventilate freely, all night if necessary and keep damping down the floors and stagings. Shade the glass.

● Prick out seedlings of pot plants sown earlier.

● Trim and feed cucumbers and tomatoes regularly and feed peppers and aubergines.

● Put those greenhouse plants that prefer lower temperatures outside but don't forget to water.

● Pinch back vines regularly and feed fruits in pots.

● Take cuttings of regal pelargoniums.

● Sow more half-hardy annuals for pot plants.

General

● Keep the sprinkler going if it's allowed.

● Turn the compost heap to accelerate rotting.

● Continue hand weeding.

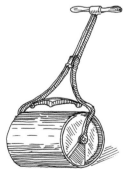

SUMMER

Kitchen garden
● Prune raspberries and tie in new canes.
● Support autumn fruiting raspberries with a single string round the whole row.
● Sow an autumn variety of lettuce.
● Prune cordon gooseberries, redcurrants, apples and pears.
● Cut off potato haulm showing symptoms of blight and harvest the crop.
● Remove old wood of briar fruits after harvesting and tie in new.
● Sow winter-hardy salad onions, winter hardy spinach or spinach beet and winter radish.
● Sow spring cabbage in a seed bed if not already done.
● Towards the end of the period sow early carrots, lettuce, raddish and turnips in the cold-frame.
● Harvest early apples and use.
● Support heavily laden branches of fruit trees.
● Protect autumn-fruiting raspberries and strawberries from birds.
● Allow a few french beans to ripen and collect and bottle them.
● Plant strawberries and pot up runners for forcing.
● Cut and dry herbs.
● Begin harvesting onions.
● Set up marrows in the sunshine to ripen.
● Begin to lift and store root vegetables.
● Remove debris from peas and beans to the compost heap but leave the roots in the ground to release nitrogen.
● Prune peaches and nectarines.
● Continue picking apples and pears.

● Earth up celery, celeriac and leeks to blanch them.
● Control cabbage white butterflies.

Flower garden
● Take clematis cuttings.
● Take cuttings of alpines, especially those that are short-lived.
● Trim conifer hedges and cut back those that have reached the required height.
● Sow and turf new lawns but be prepared to water.
● Continue mowing but leave the grass longer in dry weather.
● Sow biennials where they are to flower.
● Plant narcissi.
● Continue to feed plants in pots and baskets but change to a high nitrogen feed.
● Cut gladioli but leave some foliage to build up the corm.
● Take half-ripe shrub cuttings and softwood cuttings of geraniums, fuchsias and other tender perennials.
● Continue to dead-head roses, annuals and herbaceous perennials unless you wish to save seed.
● Continue to cut back herbaceous perennials after flowering but also continue to harvest seed where required.
● Prune rambler roses after flowering.
● Early in the period plant autumn flowering bulbs.
● Plant evergreen shrubs towards the end of the period.
● Pot up a few narcissi to fill gaps next spring.

Greenhouse, windowsill and potting shed

● Maintain continual night ventilation and damp down to keep up the humidity.

● Harvest vegetable fruits regularly, keep up the regular feeding and remove dying leaves from the bottoms of the plants.

● Sow calceolarias, schizanthus, cyclamen and primulas for pot plants.

● Pot up prepared hyacynths for Christmas flowering and plunge them outside.

● Sow winter lettuce for growing in the cold or slightly heated greenhouse.

● Repot cyclamen corms that have been resting.

● Towards the end of the period, remove shading.

● Take stem cuttings of coleus, begonias and impatiens.

AUTUMN

Kitchen garden

● Harvest and store onions, garlic and root crops.

● Plant lettuce for later cloching and spring cabbage outside.

● Harvest and store apples and pears.

● Bring ripened marrows inside to store.

● Take hardwood cuttings of gooseberries.

● As patches of soil become vacant, manure and dig them.

● Prune blackcurrants and gooseberries.

● Prune plums when they've finished cropping.

● Protect the last of the autumn-fruiting strawberries with cloches.

● Check tips of apples and pears for mildew and cut it out.

● Divide and replant rhubarb.

● Plant garlic.

● Take hardwood cuttings of currants.

● Start lifting and forcing chicory.

● Cut down tops of Jerusalem artichokes.

● Cut down asparagus and mulch with compost.

● Put greasebands round apple and cherry trees.

● Continue to pick and store apples.

● Remove yellowing leaves from brussels sprouts.

● Sow broad beans.

Flower garden

● Plant herbaceous perennials and evergreen shrubs.

● Plant deciduous trees and shrubs as soon as leaves have fallen.

● Lift, divide and replant perennials.

● Remove and compost summer bedding and replace with spring-flowering biennials.

● Replant polyanthus.

● Lift gladioli and dahlias and store the corms/tubers.

● Lift tender perennials and box them up for winter storage.

● Plant spring-flowering bulbs and lilies.

● Continue laying turf but stop mowing.

● Take cuttings of fuchsias, chrysanthemums, heathers and hydrangeas together with tender perennials.

● Rake out the thatch from the lawn, spike and topdress.

● Cut down all perennials that are over and clear away debris.

● Clean up the pool and cover with

netting to prevent leaves falling in it.
● Prune climbing and rambler roses
and weeping standards.
● Cut back the old leaves of
hellebores.
● Clip over loose growing conifers like
Chamaecyparis pisifera 'Boulevard'.
● Pick up fallen rose leaves to remove
any infected with blackspot.
● Take hardwood cuttings of deciduous
shrubs.
● Sow sweet peas in the cold-frame.
● Plant containers with bulbs and
biennials for a spring display.

Greenhouse, windowsill and potting shed
● Start to close the greenhouse at
nights and reduce watering and
damping down.
● Pot up a few root cuttings of mint
and sow a pot of parsley for the
windowsill to give a winter supply.
● Alternatively, bring a tub of herbs
into the greenhouse.

● Pot up and plunge bulbs for spring
flowering.
● Bring inside any plants that have
been standing out for the summer.
● Clear out all vegetable fruits and give
the greenhouse a good clean with a
solution of household bleach.
● Start a regular inspection of pot
plants and remove leaves attacked by
fungus.
● Pot up a few roses for early cut
flower next year.
● Pot up some early-flowering
herbaceous plants from the garden to
make good cheap pot plants.
● Bring in pot-grown chrysanthemums
and feed regularly.

General
● Clean up the garden as much as you
can for the winter, removing dead
leaves and weeds to the compost heap.
● Spread compost or manure on vacant
soil and prick it in with a fork.

Climates

Even though this is a relatively small country, there are dramatic climate variations across it. The effect of the Gulf Stream keeps the west of the country quite warm while cold northerly winds bring harsher conditions to the north. Easterlies often bring cold weather from the Russian continent and from Europe while the prevailing south-west wind tends to bring wetter weather from the Atlantic. It follows, therefore, that the east of the country is generally drier and colder than the west and the north is normally colder than the south. Height above sea level also makes a great difference to temperature and wind-chill.

So, giving accurate timings for gardening operations just isn't possible. These maps will show the differences. Gardeners living in the coldest areas should be at least two weeks behind the temperate zones while those in the warmer spots could be a fortnight ahead. If you're new to the area, take advice from the locals.

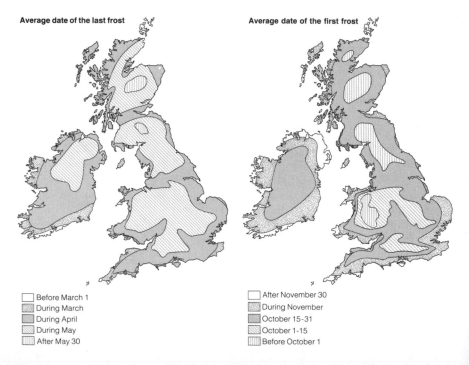

Average date of the last frost

Before March 1
During March
During April
During May
After May 30

Average date of the first frost

After November 30
During November
October 15-31
October 1-15
Before October 1

Temperature zones across Europe

EUROPE

Zone 4
−34 to −29°C
(−30 to −20°F)

Zone 5
−29 to −23°C
(−20 to −10°F)

Zone 6
−23 to −17°C
(−10 to 0°F)

Zone 7
−17 to −12°C
(0 to 10°F)

Zone 8
−12 to −7°C
(10 to 20°F)

Zone 9
−7 to −1°C
(20 to 30°F)

Zone 10
−1 to 4°C
(30 to 40°F)

The Environment and Conservation

All good gardeners are naturally conservationists at heart. It's difficult to be as close to nature as we get without becoming concerned for the wider issues. The *Gardeners' World* team is becoming increasingly involved with organizations like Butterfly Conservation and the Royal Society for the Protection of Birds simply because gardens are becoming more and more important as habitats for wildlife these days.

If you're concerned about any aspect of the environment, you'll find the appropriate organization here. They'll be pleased to help you and could certainly do with your support too.

Environmental Groups

The Barn Owl Trust
Waterleat, Ashburton, Devon
TW13 7HU

The Bat Conservation Trust
c/o Conservation Foundation
1 Kensington Gore, London SW7 2AR

British Isles Bee Breeders Association
Chamomile House, 14 Wrottesley
Road, Tettenhall, Wolverhampton
WV6 8SD

**The British Butterfly Conservation
Society Limited**
PO Box 222, Dedham, Colchester,
Essex CO7 6EY

**British Trust for Conservation
Volunteers (BTCV)**
36 St Mary's Street, Wallingford,
Oxfordshire OX10 0EU

British Trust for Ornithology
Beech Grove, Tring, Hertfordshire
HP23 5NR

Campaign for Lead-Free Air (Clear)
3 Endsleigh Street, London WC1 0DD

The Environment Council
80 York Way, London N1 9AG

**Council for the Protection of Rural
England (CPRE)**
Warwick House, 25 Buckingham
Palace Road, London SW1 0PP

Country Council for Wales
Plas Penrhos, Ffordd Penrhos, Bangor,
Gwynedd LL57 2LQ

Countryside Commission
John Dower House, Crescent Place,
Cheltenham, Gloucester GL50 3RA

English Nature
Northminster House, Northminster
Road, Peterborough, Cambs PE1 1UA

Friends of the Earth (FoE)
26-28 Underwood Street, London
N1 7JQ

Friends of the Earth (Scotland)
Bonnington Hill, 70-72 Newhaven
Road, Edinburgh EH6 5QG

Friends of the Earth Trust
26–28 Underwood Street, London
N1 7JQ

Greenpeace
30 Islington Green, London N1 8XE

**Henry Doubleday Research Association
(HDRA)**
National Centre for Organic
Gardening, Ryton-on-Dunsmore,
Coventry CV8 3LG

**International Institute for Environment
and Development (IIED)**
3 Endsleigh Street, London
WC1H 0DD

Joint Nature Conservation Committee
Monkstone House, Peterborough
PE1 1JY

London Wildlife Trust
80 York Way, London N1 9AG

Marine Conservation Society
(now incorpoating the COASTAL
ANTI-POLLUTION LEAGUE)
9 Gloucester Road, Ross-on-Wye,
Hereford & Worcester HR9 5BU

**National Federation for City Farms
(NFCF)**
The Old Vicarage, Fraser Street,
Windmill Hill, Bedminster, Bristol
NS3 4LY

National Society for Clean Air (NSCA)
136 North Street, Brighton BN1 1RG

National Trust
36 Queen Anne's Gate, London
SW1H 9AS

Ramblers Association
1–5 Wandsworth Road, London
SW8 2XX

**Royal Society for Nature Conservation
(RSNC)**
The Green, Witham Park, Lincoln
LN5 7JN

**Royal Society for the Protection of
Birds (RSPB)**
The Lodge, Sandy, Beds SG19 2DL

Scottish Heritage
12 Hope Terrace, Edinburgh EH9 2AS

Soil Association
86 Colston Street, Bristol BS1 5BB

Tidy Britain Group
The Pier, Wigan WN3 4WX

Tree Council
35 Belgrave Square, London SW1

Urban Wildlife Group
131–133 Sherlock Street, Birmingham
B5 6NB

**The Women's Environmental Network
(WEN)**
287 City Road, London EC1V 1LA

Woodland Trust
Autumn Park, Dysart Road,
Grantham, Lincs NG31 6LL

World Wide Fund for Nature (WWF)
Panda House, Weyside Park,
Godalming, Surrey GU7 1XR

Recycling Addresses

Aluminium Can Recycling Association
Suite 308, 1 Mex House, 52 Bulcher
Street, Birmingham B1 1QU

British Glass Manufacturers Federation
Northumberland Road, Sheffield
S10 2UA

British Plastics Federation
5 Belgrave Square, London
SW1X 8P0

British Waste Paper Association
Alexander House Business Centre,
Station Road, Aldershot, Hants
GU11 1BQ

Appendix I

Weights and Measures Conversion Tables

Length

10 millimetres = 1 centimetre
1,000 millimetres = 100 centimetres = 1 metre
mm = millimetres
cm = centimetres
m = metres

¼" = 6 mm
½" = 13 mm
¾" = 2 cm
1" = 2.5 cm
1½" = 4 cm
2" = 5 cm
2½" = 6.5 cm
3" = 7.5 cm
3½" = 9 cm
4" = 10 cm
4½" = 11.5 cm
5" = 12.5 cm
5½" = 14 cm
6" = 15 cm
6½" = 16.5 cm
7" = 18 cm
7½" = 19 cm
8" = 20.5 cm
8½" = 21.5 cm
9" = 23 cm
9½" = 24 cm
10" = 25.5 cm
10½" = 26.5 cm
11" = 28 cm

11½" = 29 cm
12" = 30.5 cm

1 ft = 30.5 cm
2 ft = 61 cm
3 ft = 91 cm

1 yd = 0.9 m (91 cm)
2 yd = 1.8 m
3 yd = 2.7 m
4 yd = 3.6 m
5 yd = 4.6 m
10 yd = 9.2 m
25 yd = 23 m
50 yd = 46 m
100 yd = 92 m

440 yd (¼ mile) = 400 m
880 yd (½ mile) = 800 m
1320 yd (¾ mile) = 1200 m
1760 yd (1 mile) = 1600 m

Weight

1000 grammes = 1 kilogram
g = gramme
kg = kilogram

¼ oz = 7 g
½ oz = 14 g
¾ oz = 21 g
1 oz = 28 g
1½ oz = 42 g
2 oz = 57 g
2½ oz = 71 g
3 oz = 85 g
3½ oz = 99 g
4 oz = 113 g
4½ oz = 128 g
5 oz = 142 g
5½ oz = 156 g
6 oz = 170 g
6½ oz = 184 g
7 oz = 198 g
7½ oz = 213 g
8 oz = 227 g
8½ oz = 241 g
9 oz = 255 g
9½ = 269 g
10 oz = 284 g
10½ = 298 g
11 oz = 312 g
11½ oz = 326 g
12 oz = 340 g
12½ oz = 354 g
13 oz = 369 g
13½ oz = 383 g
14 oz = 397 g
14½ oz = 411 g
15 oz = 425 g
15½ oz = 439 g
16 oz = 454 g

1 lb = 454 g
2 lb = 907 g
3 lb = 1.36 kg
4 lb = 1.81 kg
5 lb = 2.26 kg
10 lb = 4.54 kg
25 lb = 11.34 kg
50 lb = 22.68 kg
100 lb = 45.36 kg

1 stone (14lb) = 6.35 kg
1 quarter (28lb) = 12.70 kg
1 cwt (112lb) = 50.80 kg
1 ton (2240lb) = 1016 kg

1 gramme = 0.035oz
1 kilogram = 2.20lb

Area

10 000 square centimetres = 1 square
  metre
10 000 square metres = 1 hectare
sq.cm = square centimetre
sq.m = square metre

1 sq.in = 6.5 sq.cm
2 sq.in = 13 sq.cm
3 sq.in = 19 sq.cm
4 sq.in = 26 sq.cm
5 sq.in= 32 sq.cm
6 sq.in = 39 sq.cm
7 sq.in = 45 sq.cm
8 sq.in = 52 sq.cm
9 sq.in = 59 sq.cm
10 sq.in = 65 sq.cm
11 sq.in = 71 sq.cm
12 sq.in = 77 sq.cm

1 sq.ft = 930 sq.cm
2 sq.ft = 1860 sq.cm
3 sq.ft = 2790 sq.cm
4 sq.ft = 3730 sq.cm
5 sq.ft = 4650 sq.cm
6 sq.ft = 5570 sq.cm
7 sq.ft = 6500 sq.cm
8 sq.ft = 7430 sq.cm
9 sq.ft = 8360 sq.cm
10 sq.ft = 9300 sq.cm

1 sq. yd = 8360 sq.cm
2 sq.yd = 1.7 sq.m
3 sq.yd = 2.5 sq.m
4 sq.yd = 3.3 sq.m
5 sq.yd = 4.2 sq.m
6 sq.yd = 5.0 sq.m
7 sq.yd = 5.9 sq.m
8 sq.yd = 6.7 sq.m
9 sq.yd = 7.5 sq.m
10 sq.yd = 8.3 sq.m
25 sq.yd = 21 sq.m
50 sq.yd = 42 sq.m
100 sq.yd = 84 sq.m

¼ acre = 1012 sq.m
½ acre = 2024 sq.m
¾ acre = 3036 sq.m
1 acre = 4047 sq.m
2 acre = 8094 sq.m
3 acre = 1.2 hectares
4 acre = 1.6 hectares
5 acre = 2.0 hectares
10 acre = 4.0 hectares
25 acre = 10 hectares
50 acre = 20 hectares
100 acre = 40 hectares

Capacity

1000 millilitres = 1 litre
ml = millilitre

¼ pint = 142 ml
⅓ pint = 189 ml
½ pint = 284 ml
⅔ pint = 378 ml
¾ pint = 426 ml
1 pint = 568 ml
1½ pint = 852 ml
2 pint = 1.13 litres
2½ pint = 1.42 litres
3 pint = 1.70 litres
3½ pint = 1.98 litres
4 pint = 2.27 litres

4½ pint = 2.56 litres
5 pint = 2.84 litres
5½ pint = 3.12 litres
6 pint = 3.41 litres
6½ pint = 3.69 litres
7 pint = 3.98 litres
7½ pint = 4.26 litres
8 pint = 4.55 litres

¼ gal = 1.15 litres
½ gal = 2.27 litres
¾ gal = 3.41 litres
1 gal = 4.55 litres
2 gal = 9.09 litres
3 gal = 13.6 litres
4 gal = 18.2 litres
5 gal = 22.7 litres
10 gal = 45.5 litres
25 gal = 114 litres
50 gal = 228 litres
100 gal = 455 litres

1 fluid oz = 28 ml
2 fluid oz = 57 ml
3 fluid oz = 85 ml
4 fluid oz = 113 ml
5 fluid oz = 142 ml
10 fluid oz = 284 ml
20 fluid oz = 568 ml
(1 pint)

1 gill (¼ pint) = 142ml
1 quart (2 pint) = 1.13 litres

1 millilitre = 0.0017 pint
1 millilitre = 0.035 fluid oz
10 millilitre = 0.017 pint
10 millilitre = 0.35 fluid oz
50 millilitre = 0.085 pint
50 millilitre = 1.75 fluid oz
100 millilitre = 0.17 pint
100 millilitre = 3.5 fluid oz

1 litre = 1.75 pint
1 litre = 35 fluid oz

Temperature

C = Centigrade
F = Fahrenheit
Freezing points: 0°C 32°F
Boiling points: 100°C 240°F

32°F = 0°C	1°C = 34°F
35°F = 2°C	2°C = 35°F
40°F = 4°C	3°C = 37°F
45°F = 7°C	4°C = 40°F
50°F = 10°C	5°C = 41°F
55°F = 13°C	10°C = 50°F
60°F = 15°C	11°C = 52°F
65°F = 18°C	12°C = 54°F
70°F = 21°C	13°C = 55°F
75°F = 24°C	14°C = 57°F
80°F = 27°C	15°C = 60°F
85°F = 29°C	16°C = 61°F
90°F = 32°C	17°C = 63°F
95°F = 35°C	18°C = 65°F
100°F = 38°C	19°C = 66°F
105°F = 40°C	20°C = 68°F

Conversion methods

TEMPERATURE

For accurate conversion of fahrenheit readings into centigrade, take away 32, multiply by 5, then divide by 9.

For accurate conversion of centigrade readings into fahrenheit, multiply by 9, divide by 5, then add 32.

WEIGHT/AREA

To convert ounces per square yard to grams per square metre, simply multiply the ounces by 34.

Thus, 4 ounces per square yard is equal to 136 grams per square metre.

DILUTIONS

To convert fluid ounces per gallon to millilitres per litre, multiply the fluid ounces by 6.

Thus 6 fluid ounces per gallon is equal to 36 millilitres per litre.

Appendix II

Botanical Names

L atin names can be quite daunting but you should try to get to grips with them. You can see from this list that they can tell you a great deal about each particular plant. What's more, if you use the Latin name of a plant in China, Russia or Timbuctoo, they'll understand you perfectly.

Because of the peculiarities of Latin, I'm afraid that the endings of the words sometimes vary a bit. For example, *californica* means exactly the same as *californicum* and *californicus* while you might find a green leaf described as *viride* or *viridus*. Don't let that put you off any more than the pronunciation. Like any foreign language, provided you get it near enough right you'll be understood. And that's really all that matters.

Names which are geographical

atlantica – of the Atlas mountains (North Africa)
australe – southern
boreale – northern
californica – of California
cambricus – of Wales
capense – of the Cape (South Africa)
europaea – of Europe
himalaica – of the Himalaya
hispanica – of Spain
japonica – of Japan
lusitanica – of Portugal
nipponica – of Japan
occidentale – western
orientale – eastern
sinense – of China

Names describing habitat

alpina – alpine, of the Alps or growing in alpine regions
alpestris – of mountains
arvense – of fields or cultivated land
aquatica – of water, or growing by water
campestre – of plains or flat areas
littorale – of sea shores
maritima – by the sea
montana – of mountains
muralis – growing on walls
palustre – of swamps or marshes
pratense – of meadows
rivulare – of streams and brooks
rupestre – of rocks or cliffs
saxatile – rock-dwelling
sylvatica – of woods
terrestris – of the earth
uliginosus – growing in marshy places

Names describing habit

alatus – winged
arachnoides – spider- or cobweb-like
arborea – tree-like
baccatus – berried
caespitosus – tufted
columnaris – columnar
compactus – compact
compressus – compressed
contortus – twisted
erectus – upright
fastigiata – erect, the branches
frutescens – bushy
fruticosa – shrubby
giganteus – big
gramineus – grassy
horizontale – horizontally-spreading
humile – low-growing
major – greater
maximus – largest
minimus – very small
minor – lesser
nana – dwarf
parvus – small
patens – spreading
pendula – pendulous, weeping
procera – very tall, high
procumbens – procumbent, creeping
prostrata – prostrate, hugging the
  ground
pumulis – dwarf
pygmaeus – dwarf
radicans – rooting
ramosus – branched
rectus – straight
repens – creeping and rooting
sarmentosus – producing long runners
scandens – climbing
spicatus – spiny
stoloniferus – suckered
suffruticosa – woody at base
vagans – wandering

Names describing leaves

acanthifolius – prickly-leaved
angustifolia – narrow-leaved
arguta – sharp
bifoliatus – two-leaved
buxifolius – box-leaved
cordatus – heart-shaped
coriacea – coriaceous, leathery
crassifolia – thick-leaved
crispus – curled
decidua – deciduous, dropping its
  leaves
disectus – dissected
glabra – glabrous, without hairs
hederaceus – ivy-like
heterophylla – variable-leaved
hirsuta – hairy
incana – grey-downy
incisus – deeply-cut
integerrima – without teeth
laevigata – smooth and polished
lanata – woolly
latifolia – broad-leaved
macrophylla – large-leaved
maculata – spotted, blotched
marginata – margined
microphylla – small-leaved
molle – soft
nitida – shining
oppositifolius – with opposite leaves
orbicularis – rounded
ovatus – oval
parvifolia – small-leaved
picta – painted, coloured
pinnata – pinnate
platyphylla – broad-leaved
quintuplinervis – five-ribbed
reticulata – net-veined
rotundifolius – round-leaved
saponarius – soapy
sempervirens – always green,
  evergreen
serratus – sawed

splendens – glittering, shining
tomentosa – covered with a short
  dense pubescence
trifoliatus – three-leaved
triplinervis – three-ribbed
undulatus – wavy
variegata – variegated, two-coloured
velutina – velvety

Names describing flowers

barbatus – bearded
calyciformis – calyx-like
campanulata – bell-shaped
cornutus – horned
duplex – double
farinosus - floury
ferox – fertile
fimbriatus – fringed
flore-pleno – double-flowered
floribunda – free-flowering
fragrans – scented
grandiflora – large-flowered
labiatus – lipped
macropetala – many-petalled
nudiflora – naked, without leaves
nutans – nodding
octandrus – with eight stamens
paniculata – flowering in panicles
parviflora – small-flowered
pauciflora – few-flowered
pectinatus – comb-like
pedunculatus – stalked
pleniflorus – with double flowers
plumosus – feathered
polyantha – many-flowered
punctatus – finely-spotted
racemosa – flowers in racemes
spicata – flowers in spikes
stellata – starry
tigrinus – spotted
triflora – flowers in threes
umbellata – flowers in umbels
uniflora – one-flowered

Names describing colours

aethiopicus – black
alba – white
albicans – nearly white
albidus – off white
argentea – silvery
atro – black
atro-coccineus – crimson black
atro-purpureus – purple black
atrovirens – deep green
aurantiaca – orange
auratus – gilded
aurea – golden
bicolor – two-coloured
caerulea – blue
candicans – becoming white
cardinalis – cardinal red
carneus – flesh-coloured
chlorinus – yellow green
cinerea – ash grey
citrinus – lemon yellow
coccinea – scarlet
coloratus – coloured
concolor – of the same colour
cupreus – copper-coloured
dealbatus – whitened
discolor – two-coloured
erythrinus – red
ferreus – iron grey
ferruginea – rusty brown
flava – pale yellow
flavissimus – intense yellow
galanthus – milky white
glauca – sea green
hepaticus – liver-coloured
igneus – flame-coloured
incanus – grey
juniperinus – blue brown
lactea – milky white
lilacina – lilac
lividus – grey purple
lutea – yellow
lutescens – becoming yellow

marginatus – edged with another colour
melleus – honey-coloured
nigellus – nearly black
nigra – black
nivalis – pure white
ochraceus – yellow ochre
pallidus – pale
primulinus – sulphury yellow
punicea – crimson
purpurea – purple
rosea – rose-coloured
rubra – red
sanguinea – blood red
sulphureus – sulphur yellow
tricolor – three-coloured
variegata – variegated two-coloured
versicolor – variously-coloured, or changing colour
violacea – violet
virens – green
viride – green

Names describing aromas and scents

aromatica – aromatic
citriodora – lemon-scented
foetida – strong-smelling, unpleasant
fragrans – fragrant
fragrantissima – most fragrant
graveolens – smelling unpleasantly
odorata – sweet-scented
odoratissima – sweetest-scented
moschata – musk-scented
suaveolens – sweet-scented

Names alluding to other plants

bignonoides – bignonia-like
jasminea – jasmine-like
liliiflora – lily-flowered

pseudoplatanus – false plane
quercifolius – oak-leaved
rosaceus – rose-like
salicifolia – willow-leaved
tulipifera – tulip-bearing

Names which are commemorative

delavayi – after the Abbé Delavay
douglasi – after David Douglas
fargesii – after Père Farges
farreri – after George Farrer
forrestii – after George Forrest
foryunei – after Robert Fortune
fraseri – after John Fraser
harryana – after Sir Harry Veitch
henryana (um)(us) – after Dr Augustine Henry
hookeri – after Sir Joseph Hooker
mariesii – after Charles Maries
thunbergii – after Carl Peter Thunberg
veitchii – after John Gould Veitch
vilmorinii – after Maurice de Vilmorin
williamsiana (um)(us) – after Mr J C Williams
willmottiana (um)(us) – after Miss Ellen Willmott
wilsoniae – after Mrs E H Wilson

Miscellaneous names

acaulis – stemless
aestivus – summer
affine – related (to another species)
amabile – lovely
ambigua – doubtful (identity ?)
amoenus – charming, pleasing
bella – pretty
biennis – biennial
brilliantissimus – very brilliant
bulbiferus – bulb-bearing
calceolaria – slipper-shaped
ceriferus – waxy

commune – common, occuring in plenty
confusa – confused (identity ?)
crenatus – scalloped
crispa – curly
cristatus – crested
cruciformus – cross-shaped
cuneatus – wedge-shaped
cuspidatus – pointed
cylindricus – cylindrical
cymbiformis – boat-shaped
decorus – handsome
deformis – misshapen
dentata – toothed
dependens – hanging down
dissimilis – unlike
dulce – sweet
echinatus – spined
edule – edible
elatior – higher
elegans – elegant
exiguus – small, scant
fibrosus – fibrous
flabellatus – fan-shaped
flaccidus – weak
florida – free-flowering
formosa – handsome, beautiful
fragalis – fragile
frigidus – cold
glabellus – smooth
gracilis – slender
gladiolus – little sword
globosus – ball-shaped
glutinosus – sticky
grandis – large
gutatus – spotted
hortensis – of gardens
hybrida – hybrid
insigne – outstanding
integerrimus – whole

intermedia (um)(us) – intermediate
laciniatus – fringed
laevigatus – smooth
lanuginosus – downy
laxus – loose
lentus – pliable
lineatus - finely-lined
littoralis – of the sea shore
lucidus – clear, shining
maculatus – spotted
media – middle, midway between
mollis – tender
nervatus – of the shop (herbal)
officinale – of the shop (herbal)
oxalis – acid (taste)
perennis – perennial
plicata – folded
praecox – early
praestans – excellent
pulchella – beautiful
rigens – rigid
rugosus – wrinkled
sativa – sown, planted or cultivated
scaber – rough
speciosa – splendid
spectabalis – showy
splendens – brilliant
squamatus – scaley
sterilis – barren
striata – striped
terminulis – terminal
tuberosus – tuberous
tubularis – flat
tulipa – turban
utile – useful
validus – strong
ventricocus – swollen
vernale – spring
vulgare – common
zebrinus – striped